THE MYSTERIOUS SENSES
OF ANIMALS

THE MYSTERIOUS
SENSES OF
ANIMALS

by
VITUS B. DRÖSCHER

Translated from the German by
Eveleen Huggard

1965
E. P. DUTTON & CO., INC.
New York

Line drawings in this book were executed by H. Skaruppe after
originals in the periodicals listed below, or other sources speci-
fied, or after drawings by the author.
Natur und Museum, XCII (1962). *Natur und Volk,* LXXXIV
(1954); XCI (1961). *Naturwissenschaftliche Rundschau,* XIII
(1960). Photograph by Paul Popper Ltd. *Scientific American*
(December, 1958; August, 1959; October, 1959; October, 1960;
December, 1960; July, 1961; December, 1961; February, 1962;
March, 1962). *Umschau,* LVIII (1958); LIX (1959); LXI
(1961); LXII (1962). Von Frisch, Karl, *Aus dem Leben der
Bienen* (Berlin: Springer Verlag, 1953). Wiehle, H., *Aus dem
Spinnenleben Wärmerer Länder* (Wittenberg: A. Ziemsen Verlag,
1954). *Zeitschrift für Tierpsychologie,* XIII (1956); XVI
(1959).

Library of Congress Catalog Card Number: 64-21859

CONTENTS

5 ,

ILLUSTRATIONS

[1]Walter Wissenbach
[2]Wide World Photos
[3]United Press International
[4]Popperphoto
[5]Walt Disney's True Life Production 'Nature's Half Acre'
[6]Friedel Doering
[7]German Press Agency
[8]Comet-Photo
[9]Toni Angermayer
[10]Herr Hanisch
[11]Kurt Wyss

Line drawings by H. Skaruppe, Hamburg.

I

BEYOND THE FIVE SENSES

Listening in to the Enemy Transmitter

CHANCE often plays a vital part in exciting discoveries. So it was on a warm summer evening in 1956, when Kenneth D. Roeder, Professor of Physiology at Tufts University, Medford, Mass., was giving a party for his friends on his garden terrace. Chinese lanterns were lit, and were at once surrounded by the whirr of a giddy host of moths. When the evening wore on one of those present did what many a wine-drinker had done before. He ran a dampened cork round the rim of his glass, causing the familiar shrill, ringing tone. At that moment it happened.

The moths which had been fluttering round the lanterns immediately dropped to the ground. At first Dr. Roeder thought they had been killed or paralysed by the high, nerve-racking sound. There are examples enough among animals of convulsions, sometimes fatal, caused by loud noises.

But, to the surprise of the whole company, the moths were alive and alert. They crawled about for a while, and then began to fly again. But as soon as the glass was made to 'sing', they again dropped to the ground like inanimate objects.

This curious behaviour has incidentally long been turned to account by butterfly collectors to catch the night 'colleagues' of the day moths with lamp, cork, wine-glass and net. But as a result of this incident Professor Roeder and his colleague Dr. Asher E. Treat, of the City College of New York, were the first to investigate the phenomenon scientifically. The results surpassed their wildest expectations.

They began by playing the whole musical scale, now loudly, now softly, from loudspeakers and sound generators, to all the

9

many hawk-moths, spinner-moths, looper-moths, owlets and leaf-roller moths. In doing so they found that moths of many different species, particularly of the Noctuid family, are sensitive to musical notes. Even to sound waves pitched too high to be audible to the human ear, they react by instantly dropping to the ground. Why moths, in contrast to most other insects, can hear musical notes, and why they react in this way, at first remained mysterious. But one day illumination came. The two scientists found that moths had exceptionally high sensitivity in the so-called ultrasonic range if the sound was exactly like that transmitted by bats orienting themselves by sound during their insect hunts at night.

So many moths can hear the 'transmitter' of their greedy foes. The ultrasonic broadcast of a bat means the imminent danger of being eaten, and consequently it is high time to take evasive action. Not until after the careful research of these two American scientists did we gain a full realisation of the crafty devices, the weapons and counter-weapons, by which nocturnal ultrasonic warfare between bats and moths is conducted.

The moths' 'ears' were found in pairs between the thorax and the abdomen, thus near their 'waist'. Their construction is as ingenious as it is simple. A tiny air space is covered on the outside by a fine tympanic membrane. Inside there are three microscopically small sensory nerve cells. Vibrations caused in the membrane by sound waves in turn cause the sensory nerve cells to send 'Morse signals' to the insect's brain.

The two scientists resolved to intercept these signals to discover how the moth behaves in face of danger. They tapped the nerve fibres of the three sensory cells with needles so fine that a thousand bunched together would fill out the head of an ordinary pin.

Such an operation cannot, of course, be performed by hand. The needle, which is invisible to the naked eye, has to be inserted under a stereo-microscope with the aid of a micromanipulator. This ultra-fine intervention has the advantage of doing no perceptible injury to the living moth. Thus it can be clipped to a mount, the electric 'Morse signals' of the pricked nerve can be amplified and relayed to a kind of television screen or into a loudspeaker. This makes it possible to trace accurately the signals sent to the moth's brain by the three sensory cells when a bat approaches in the evening sky.

Two-stage Warning

The warning system operates as soon as a bat approaches within thirty yards. The 'A' cells begin to send out impulses, at first in slow and regular succession, then gaining pace with the enemy's closer approach.

Coming from both 'ears', these signals do not synchronise in reaching the moth's brain. According to whether the bat approaches from left or right, the single impulses are displaced against each other either more or less, but always in a quite characteristic fashion. The moth can rely on this information to carry out the correct evasive manoeuvre in good time, sometimes even before the bat has noticed it.

Insect-hunting by bats is therefore no simple matter, and these uncanny fluttering mammals might be in a bad way had they not developed an antidote to the skilful evasive manoeuvres of their prey. This is their reeling flight. However awkward, clumsy and senseless it appears, in reality it is a meaningful zigzag course plotted with precision and subtlety to deceive the moths about their true route.

When a bat approaches within six yards the 'B' cells in the moth's 'ears' begin to send out alarm signals. This brings about a sudden and violent change in its behaviour, for two reasons. In the first place the bat has located its prey and is approaching it in direct flight. Secondly, the moth is now no longer capable, for physical reasons, of recognising from which direction the enemy is approaching. The two Americans filmed bats bearing down on free-flying moths, and were thus able to observe each separate phase in detail. When the danger grows acute, that is, when the 'B' cells release the second alarm, moths of several species fold back their wings and drop to earth like a bomb.

But the bat, too, changes its course. It actually seems to have the capacity of calculating simple ballistic trajectories in pursuing its prey. Analysis of some hundreds of film shots showed that, in six cases out of ten, the bat catches its prey even when it has dropped to the ground. If it fails to catch it with its mouth, it tries to net it with extended wing.

Thus it is that during the course of evolution some types of moth have developed which in emergency drop swiftly to the ground, or after an abrupt change of direction gyrate to earth in narrow spirals. With these tactics they have a much better chance of survival, because the bat nearly always shoots past them.

The third sensory nerve cell in the moth's 'ear' incessantly transmits signals the meaning of which is still obscure. We know only that the sequence of impulses changes when the parts of the animal's body become twisted towards one another. Obviously another great secret lies hidden here, a secret you would never suspect when you watch a moth fluttering round a lamp.

Ears that 'See'

Bats use devices that are just as cunning. It has been known since the forties that they utter ultrasonic sounds inaudible to the human ear and use the echoes to locate obstacles or their prey. As Professor Möhres, of Tübingen, and Professor Griffin, of Harvard, have shown, this discovery was only the gateway to a world full of mysterious wonders inhabited by these uncanny creatures.

The lesser horseshoe bat can 'see' with its ultrasonic ears at night better than a human eye can see by day. If wires only 0.2 millimetres in diameter are stretched across a room, and if they do not glisten in the sunlight, a human being unaware of their presence will run blindly into them. Not so the lesser horseshoe bat, even in the dark. It will not touch the wires, however many there may be, and even if they are all criss-crossed and tangled.

That gave the scientists an idea. They wanted to find out whether a bat with its 'sonar' (that is the technical term for a radar apparatus which operates with sound instead of with radio waves) can only locate obstacles and insects that lie in front of its nose, or has a panoramic view of its surroundings.

A big university lecture hall was divided into two parts with tennis nets, and some meshes were cut, forming a hole low down on one side. A human being was able to discover the hole only in a good light and after much searching. Then the hall

Lesser horseshoe bat in flight.

was darkened, and a bat was released from a wooden box. Without a moment's hesitation it flew straight through the hole. So there is no doubt that a bat can 'see' its surroundings with its ears, with the same or perhaps greater distinctness than a man can see his surroundings in the dark in the light cone of a pocket torch. In other words, it sees with its ears.

To accomplish this feat of sense perception incomprehensible to us human beings, the lesser horseshoe bat possesses a remarkable transmitting apparatus. Its exceptionally large and muscular larynx produces ultra-high sounds of 110,000 vibrations a second, which are emitted through the nose. Its nostrils are surrounded by a horseshoe-shaped 'moon crater', which like a reflector mirror focuses the sound waves and aims them at a particular target.

The ultrasonic sounds incessantly emitted, audible to a man only as a low crackle if he keeps his ear directly in front of the animal's head, are louder to the bat then the rattle of a machine-gun is to a man. At dusk, when bats fly by the hundred and thousand from eaves, old arched roofs and castle ruins on their hunt for insects, for them the air is filled with the inferno of battle.

In a noisy throng of human beings you cannot even hear yourself speak, but a bat can distinguish the echoes of its own screams in the crackle of hundreds of machine-guns, so to speak, and it never hesitates in its flight. Sometimes a bat observes another heading towards an insect. It is able to identify it by its voice, and knows whether it is a stranger, or a bat weaker than itself. If it is the latter, it emits an ultrasonic warning scream and snatches the prey from under the finder's nose.

Instrument Flying from Memory

The receiving system of the bat's ears is still more extraordinary. In normal flight both auricles are pointed forward in the direction of flight. If the horseshoe bat intends to make a curvilinear flight, split seconds beforehand its ears are directed in the flight direction intended. From this too it is evident that the bat's reeling flight is in reality deliberate.

If, however, the bat discovers an obstacle or a potential prey, the ears at once begin to beat back and forth in opposite directions up to six times a second. In the process they receive echoes from many directions – weak ones from distant objects or those with poor reflecting capacity, and strong ones from near by.

The whole environment in this way is 'scanned' dot by dot and line by line, and assembled in the bat brain as a mosaic or screen to form a picture. It corresponds completely to the optical impression gained for us by the eyes.

Moreover, the animal, through its locomotion during flight and through the double impression in the two ears, obtains an accurate notion of space. An absolutely fantastic achievement of its nervous system.

People often say: 'I could find my way home in my sleep.' Even so, they have to keep a watchful eye open so as not to stumble over kerbstones, and they have to make sure that they turn into the right street at the right time and do not run into a wall. Only the blind learn their way, step by step, by heart, yet from time to time they feel with a stick to make sure of their direction.

Bats, however, have in their head a precise sound picture of every detail in the neighbourhood of their home, where they fly by memory only, blind as well as deaf, although, because of their efficient sonar system, they would seem to have no need of this enormous mental effort. A simple experiment demonstrated the creatures' memory. While they were out hunting at night, the opening of their cavern home was blocked with a board. Towards morning the homing bats in hundreds dashed against it full tilt.

Professor Griffin tells of a tame bat which by established custom slept in a big bird-cage in his room. It invariably flew through the little door, which was always kept open. This involved it in a by no means simple S-bend. One day the professor removed all the bars and glass walls. In spite of this the bat continued for weeks to negotiate the same S-bend on every entrance and exit flight at the precise spot where the tiny entrance had been.

Finally Professor Griffin took away the small 'horizontal bar' on which the animal used to hang. In landing on a bar or branch the bat approaches in a bird-like attitude, brakes with wings drawn up, stretches out its legs, clings tight and then dangles backwards underneath. Professor Griffin's bat approached like this, clutched with its feet at the void, and fell to the floor of the cage. Not till after this mishap did it use its sound-echoing apparatus. It suspended itself on a ring and now discovered for the first time that the glass walls and bars of the cage had been removed.

Flying insects are not the only victims of bats, which can scan the earth's surface like a bomber with its radar. If a beetle rustles in the grass at night, a bat can hear it. Soundlessly it glides down, settles purposefully next to it, and eats it.

In South-West Africa scorpions are the favourite dish of hunting bats. They seize arachnids, so intimidating to other living creatures, by the raised poison-sting tail, carry them to a branch from which they can suspend themselves, bite off the poisonous sting, hold the disarmed prey in a wing half folded like an umbrella, and eat it with healthy appetite.

Now comes what sounds like a fisherman's story. There are four types of bat that catch fish. In pitch darkness they fly close to the surface of the water, suddenly plunge in feet foremost, pull out a wriggling fish and put it straight in their mouth. The question is: How do they detect the fish swimming just below the surface? For all his technical skill, man cannot do this. An aircraft cannot locate a submerged submarine unless it drops a special buoy which relays to it by radio the submarine's underwater bearings. The reason is that when airborne sound strikes the surface of the water, nearly all of it is reflected back into the air. Only about a thousandth part of the sound energy passes on as water sound. Of this the submarine (or fish) reflects only a fraction, and of this again a mere fraction reaches the air. What finally comes back into the aircraft's receiving system (or the bat's ears) is a million times less than the sound re-echoed normally.

That is why the physicists regard it as impossible. What cannot be done despite decades of endeavour by thousands of scientists in the expensively equipped laboratories of the world's naval and air forces could hardly be done by a small bat.

But Professor Griffin sticks to his point. He maintains that there is no other rational explanation. The bats with their ultrasonic transmitters and receivers can, he says, locate fish swimming under water. And he adds: 'Instead of squandering millions of dollars to no purpose, it would be better to set about penetrating the secret of the bats.' Perhaps we can learn from the world of animals how it is done.

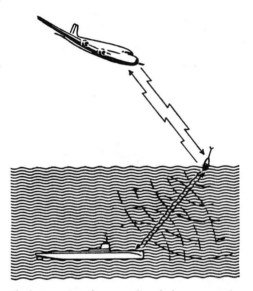

In contrast to the bat, an aircraft cannot directly locate an underwater target. Man can do so only with the aid of information relayed from a special buoy equipped with a transmitter.

It has nearly always been so. Only after man has made a technical invention does he discover that nature made it long before. This is certainly flattering to human vanity, but is too late to serve any practical purpose.

American scientists have therefore established a new branch of research called bionics. Its aim is to ferret out the secrets still concealed in the bosom of nature with a view to their practical application. The puzzling faculties of the bat are only one point of departure.

Another thing about which we are completely in the dark is how bats, taken by car in a dark box 200 miles from their home, are able to find their way back again in the shortest possible time, that is to say, as the crow flies, though by day they are nearly blind and have no knowledge of the area to which they are taken.

We shall return to this phenomenon in the chapter on the riddles of animal migration.

The Dolphin's Sonar

The great art of seeing with the ears is not exclusive to bats. Whales, and in particular dolphins and porpoises, mammals of the sea, perform astonishing feats of this kind. They actually have two different sound transmission systems with which they find their way about the ocean and make 'radio contact' with one another.

The sonar of the dolphin produces ghostly tones in the water rather as if a pebble were knocked on glass. German U-boat crews knew and dreaded that sound. During the Battle of the Atlantic it was a sure sign that they had been picked up by an underwater position-finder.

The position-finders constructed by human beings, when once they have found a target, go ticking on with the same even beat, but dolphins have a more cunning device. The simple ticking, which in man-made sonar, in Goethe's phrase, is 'wisdom's last conclusion', is transmitted by the sea mammals only for general reconnaissance when they perceive no reaction anywhere. But when they receive the first echoes, they are not satisfied with knowing that something or other is there, they want details. The ticking grows faster and faster, and changes into something like the creaking of a badly oiled door and finally the scream of a circular saw.

If the dolphin thinks it has located a fish, it makes a bee-line for it at its top speed of about twenty miles an hour, with continuous head oscillations of some 10 degrees to right and left, so that it can constantly check its bearings until it has reached its victim. Also, in contrast to the echolots and sonar apparatus made by human hands, it transmits, not on a single wavelength, but on a broad band, including both low and ultra-high waves. The advantages of this are inestimable.

The low tones penetrate to a depth of a few miles in the water, which below thirty feet is dark as night, and provide the dolphin with a survey of what goes on in the distance. The ultrasonic tones, used for close-range work, are clearly distinguishable in spite of the jamming noises of every kind that fill the sea-depths which are ostensibly so still. These would otherwise turn the dolphin's sonar into 'misted spectacles'.

The chief jammers are the barely finger-size shrimps, small crustaceans, which appear in legions in certain sea areas, more especially during the Antarctic summer. With their greedy, plankton-cracking claws they create such an uproar that dolphins in these sea areas would lose their bearings without ultrasonics, and would recognise neither friend nor foe nor prey.

Can dolphins with their sonar in fact distinguish friend from foe, a porpoise from a shark or sperm-whale? To find out whether dolphins, like bats, can 'hear' pictures, Professor Wood carried out an experiment in the Marineland Oceanarium at St. Augustine, Florida, which is familiar from many news-reels. The experiment was similar to the bat experiment carried out in the lecture hall divided by tennis nets. This time a spacious swimming bath was divided into two by means of a wire grating. On the left and on the right escape slits were left open, just big enough for a dolphin to slip through. But this time there was an additional refinement. The two holes in the grating could be blocked alternately with a pane of plexiglass. For a man to have to decide at a distance of several yards which hole was suitable for him to dive through would have been a complete gamble, but for the dolphins the water was made muddy into the bargain; they could not have seen their fins before their eyes. In spite of these difficulties they invariably and unerringly made for the right hole, as sight-lines clearly showed, and even from a distance were not once misled by the plexiglass.

Here was an incontestable demonstration of the 'optical view' with which their sonar apparatus provides these lovable

water acrobats. They should be capable of identifying the out-
lines of every fish and of distinguishing a shoal of herrings
from a patch of seaweed and a swordfish from a barracuda.
When will man's technical skill have reached the same level?

Dolphin Talk

Now for the dolphin's other mysterious sound transmitter.
With it he emits whistling notes which sound like the cheeping of a canary, but are considerably louder. At first it was
thought that these were simply squeals of emotion, rather like a
pig's when it is kept waiting for food. But the dolphin's
utterances seem to be on a much higher level.

Professor Kellogg, of Chicago University, from his motor
yacht equipped with underwater microphones, observed how
dolphins which live sociably in so-called schools of five, ten or
even several hundred members, maintain voice contact with
one another by four whistles a minute, to avoid dispersal in
turbid or deep water.

Furthermore, during the mating period he heard loud
whining and howling, reminiscent of the moonlight concerts
of cats on the roof. The plaintive tones sounded like a baby's
crying. At other times dolphins may make a soft and gentle
droning sound or break out into staccato squeaking or bleating.
If a fish is held out for tame dolphins in an oceanarium to
jump for, and it is repeatedly snatched away in front of their
noses, they utter really heart-rending wails.

Do all these sounds add up to a kind of language? We do not
yet know. The American zoologist, Dr. John C. Lilly, however, is a fanatical champion of this hypothesis, and what he
has to say claims the attention of others besides specialists. It
has actually been conjectured that there may be species in the
animal kingdom which dispute man's prerogative of communicating by sound language.

As a child Dr. Lilly was obsessed by the idea of talking to
animals, learning their language or teaching them human
words and their meaning. In 1955 he thought of the dolphin

as a possibility. He might perhaps have found a suitable land animal among the baboons, for instance, to experiment with, but dolphins fascinated him, because they can mimic human laughter and speech sounds with greater virtuosity than a parrot, show high intelligence and imaginative talent in play, and can make friends with man. Also, the dolphin brain is strikingly similar to the human, in proportion to weight, in its wealth of convolutions, and the structure of the nerve cells.

In order to make a closer study of dolphinese, Dr. Lilly had two dolphins swimming around in a tank which was divided by a metal sheet into two basins, so that the two could not see but could only hear each other. With underwater microphones, special tapes and sound spectrographs he recorded 'conversations' of up to twenty minutes' length between them. Sometimes the duologue was preceded by long monologues, with which one dolphin evidently intended to stimulate its partner into volubility. In general, conversation was carried on, not only with very high whistling notes, but also with a tremendous swiftness of speech which a human with the best will in the world could not follow.

What the two dolphins were discussing so freely of course remained obscure to Dr. Lilly, for we still lack any clues from which to infer the meaning of the sound combinations. But, even so, it was possible for a dolphin alphabet to be formulated.

A dolphin whistle lasts for about half a second, and in this short time changes in pitch in a way scarcely perceptible to the human ear, but it is entirely characteristic, for example, low-high or high-low, or low-high-low, and so on. So far, twelve different whistling signals have been registered, supposedly representing a kind of alphabet, for they are always transmitted coherently in different combinations, rather as with us a word is a combination of letters.

When a critic objected that after all the years of experiment the dolphins, in view of their allegedly great intelligence, should long ago have grasped what it was all about, Dr. Lilly replied that if the dolphins had been trying to make contact with us during all these years, they would certainly have been greatly disheartened at our stupidity.

Whether or not the strange whistling signals in the ocean are a 'dolphinese language' or some completely mysterious phenomenon from the world of the senses, we can certainly look forward to the progress of these experiments with great interest.

Palaver Under Water

In the spring of 1962 Dr. Lilly received unexpected support from the American Air Force and from engineers of the Lockheed Aircraft Corporation. For these the sounds of dolphins and the near relations of these sea mammals, the porpoises, were originally a thorn in the flesh, misleading or interfering with the sonar and other underwater sound detectors of the anti-submarine defence force. On this account they were obliged to study the ocean palaver of these animals.

So one day they carried out an experiment. Across the entrance to a lagoon on the Pacific coast of California they placed at twenty-metre intervals fifteen spar buoys with a draught of three metres. They also installed two underwater microphones close by, and awaited the outcome with loud-speakers and tape-recorders in a boat.

Late in the afternoon they sighted five porpoises at a distance of 500 metres. The instruments registered an acceleration of the familiar ultrasonic click. Thus the animals with their sonar had already discovered that something suspicious was in their way. They slowed down the tempo, and when they had approached within 400 metres swam into shallow shore waters and collected there in a compact group.

Presently one porpoise left the group and crossed cautiously from one buoy to another. When it returned to its companions a concert of shrill whistling notes and almost hurricane violence burst out in the water. The outcome of this 'conference' was that a second scout swam out to inspect the objects of general displeasure. On its return there was once more a lively whistling session. Only then did feelings calm down. The porpoises left the shallow water, felt their way forward carefully, clicking continually, but otherwise silent, and disappeared in the lagoon.

The Lockheed engineers were convinced that the whistling concert was a lively conference on the situation. The details of what passed between the animals of course remained impenetrable. It may be assumed, however, that the conversation turned on the problem of whether this line of buoys perhaps had something to do with the devilish fish-nets of men or was dangerous in some novel way.

It may be added that in 1959 the American marine biologist Dr. Lessmann made a similar discovery. He demonstrated that those fabulous deep-sea fish that bring slight illumination to the eternal night in the depths of the oceans with their natural headlights actually signal with them. Evidently these creatures of darkness have a code with which they summon their spouses, warn rivals and perhaps communicate with each other about other things as well.

The 'Third Eye' of the Rattlesnake

The 'seeing' ultrasonic ears of bats and dolphins are not the only examples of unusual ultra-senses in the animal kingdom. In 1958 Professor Bullock, of California University, chanced on a 'third eye' of an entirely different kind when he was investigating the problem of how it was possible for the rattlesnake to ferret out its prey — mice, rats, other small warm-blooded animals and lizards — in total darkness.

At night mice can see practically nothing. They grope about with their sensitive 'whiskers' and learn by heart every path in the hunting-ground they constantly patrol, so that in case of danger they can quickly and unerringly reach their hole. As with bats, which know by heart the flight routes near their sleeping-places, the small rodents' memory turns night into day.

With its tongue the rattlesnake examines the ground, blades

of grass and stones until it discovers a fresh scent of mice from the odour molecules shed by the latter. These it continually strips with its palate, which is equipped with an exceptionally subtle sense of smell. Thus it pursues the mouse while it trips fearlessly to and fro nibbling at this and that.

But how does the snake know when it is close enough to its victim? How does it know precisely where the mouse will be, when it wants to strike across a distance of half a yard with its fangs protruding?

It might be assumed that the rattlesnake had phenomenally good eyes and was able to make out its prey in the dark. To test this, a rattlesnake and a mouse were shut up together in a small terrarium, the reptile was blindfolded with adhesive plaster, and a chemical fluid was sprayed into its mouth to obstruct the gustatory nerves. Failure to find its victim would demonstrate that after all it found its way about at night with the aid of its eyes.

Professor Bullock waited to see what would happen. It was evident at once that the rattlesnake had no intention of playing 'blind man's buff' with the mouse. It obviously knew exactly in which direction its victim was running at any moment. It followed resolutely, tensed itself like a steel spring, darted forward, and ten minutes later the mouse had half disappeared down its throat.

It had not been able to see, smell or hear its victim (snakes are deaf), or find it by touch, but it caught it with uncanny assurance. Were unknown rays at work here, or a mysterious sense not accessible to us human beings?

When he examined the rattlesnake's body, Professor Bullock noticed two small, trough-shaped cavities which, like car headlights, lay on either side of the reptile's head between nostril and eye. Was the answer to be looked for here? What would happen if they were covered with adhesive plaster? The snake was again placed in the terrarium, the light was turned out, and at least a dozen mice were put in with it. Days later it had not caught a single mouse. Only when the two dimples were covered was the rattlesnake really 'blind'.

. What strange type of sense organ could be concealed in these dimples? In the thin skin covering the cavities Professor Bullock found sensory nerve cells which turned out to be less unfamiliar than he had expected, for they are also present in the human skin and enable us to feel heat. But, whereas man on a square centimetre of skin has only about three of these 'heat spots', a similar area of the rattlesnake dimple contains

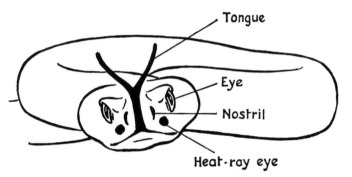

Front view of a rattlesnake's head.

no fewer than 150,000 sensory nerve cells. This agglomeration of cells sensitive to heat raises the temperature sense of the rattlesnake to an extraordinary level, enabling it to 'see' heat rays, not only those from a red-hot furnace, but also those from the body of a mouse or other animal or object. If human beings possessed such infra-red eyes, a public meeting at night would seem like a swarm of outsize glow-worms.

The dimples, or pits, are rather like reflector mirrors in shape. Thus the rattlesnake can receive heat rays only from two severely limited conical areas. By swinging its head from side to side it can discover the presence of a warm-blooded animal, and also perceive its approximate size and shape. It is probably capable of distinguishing a rat from a snake-eating mongoose.

If an electric light bulb, switched off but still hot, is wrapped in cloth and held in front of a rattlesnake in the dark, it will strike out at it. The heat-ray picture it receives must therefore be something like a view through misted spectacle lenses.

Incidentally, the 'third eye' is very useful to the snake when hunting by day. There are a number of lizards and salamanders which are capable of deceptively adapting themselves to their surroundings in shape and colour. With its true eyes the snake cannot detect such creatures, but its heat-ray eye spots them immediately.

This example shows that faculties that seem mysterious at first sight may depend on perfectly normal and familiar physiological facts. No 'super'-physics, but rational adaptation of long familiar things leads to the development of phenomena as extraordinary as this heat-discerning 'eye'.

How Does It Find the Mussel?

The sighting mechanism with which the Ephialtis ichneumon fly takes a bearing on its victim is another example that far exceeds the capacities of human senses. Sometimes the animal can be observed running to and fro on a tree-trunk, obviously searching for something. Suddenly it stops, corrects its position by a few millimetres, and then drives its six-centimetre-long, fine-toothed borer into the wood with remarkable speed.

If the tree-trunk is sawed open, it will be found that the fly has accurately pierced and laid an egg in a pupa or larva concealed in the wood, the presence of which we with our senses would have been unable to detect.

Oil prospectors who, in spite of technically correct sound-bearings and a thorough knowledge of geology, often find they have bored in the wrong place, may well envy the faculties of this insect.

However, our ideas about the technique with which the ichneumon fly infallibly tracks down its victim concealed in the wood are still vague.

It used to be thought that it perhaps had an exceptionally

sensitive thermometer with which it detected the larva by its body temperature, or had a sound detector with which it located the mining noises of the creature boring in the wood. Woodpeckers are very successful in this sound-detecting operation. Every cracking, grinding or ticking noise concealed behind wood arouses in them a fanatical eagerness to drum and devour. If a ticking alarm-clock is hidden in a wooden chest and this is left standing in a forest, in a very short time it will most certainly be drummed to bits by woodpeckers scenting out prey.

But, whereas woodpeckers will go for practically anything that makes a noise in rotten tree-trunks, Ephialtis ichneumon flies are decidedly fastidious. One type (in Germany alone there are more than 1,000 different kinds) is interested only in the pupa of longhorn beetles. Another seeks only the larvae of the horntail or closely related sawfly and finds them without ever making the mistake of boring at a wrong host animal.

This behaviour is a harsh necessity for the preservation of the species. If the ichneumon fly's egg were laid in the wrong kind of larva or pupa, it would perish, because the victim would die before an ichneumon fly larva, and from it in turn a viable ichneumon fly pupa, had developed from the egg. On the other hand, the host must not be too vital or too long-lived, as in that case it destroys the egg in its body or devours the ichneumon fly larva as it slips out. Thus almost every little wood-dweller has its own special type of ichneumon fly for an enemy, which seeks it alone and by means of it alone can ensure the continuance of its kind.

This means, however, that a sound detector or heat-ray eye must probably be ruled out as the scenting sense of the ichneumon fly, for with these the insect could hardly distinguish a useless pupa from a desirable longhorn beetle pupa. The tendency today is to assume an exceptionally subtle sense of smell with which the ichneumon fly picks up the body exhalations of the wood parasites through the fine pores in the wood. Research into the details of this fantastic sense achievement still remains to be carried out.

One of the most primitive organisms on earth, the starfish, possesses a similarly inexplicable sense. This echinoderm attacks clams (oysters, etc.) lying on the sea-bed, tears the two shells apart with its arms, turns out its own stomach upside down over the soft parts of the prey, and digests it outside its body. But how does it find the clams if, as is usually the case, they are hidden in the sand? What nobody would have believed possible on this scale was observed in 1961 by Dr.

A starfish raises itself on its five arms to pull a clam it has located out of the sand and eat it.

S. L. Smith on the Pacific coast of Washington State. A ten-inch starfish creeping over the sand of the sea bottom suddenly twitched slightly, returned to a spot it had just travelled over, and began to dig. Strange to say, it did so without using its five powerful arms. It used some thirty of its hundred odd tiny, retractable suckers to shovel up the sand at a rhythmical pace. Ultimately it had dug a sandpit two feet three inches in diameter and four inches deep at the centre. Anyone who has ever tried to dig a sandpit by hand under water will be able to appreciate the starfish's achievement.

An unsuccessful boring would no doubt have unpleasant consequences for the creature's physical state. But it is a safe bet that it finds its victim exactly in the middle of the sandpit every time. The suckers of the central disc cling fast to the shell. Then it levers itself up on the arm points, pulls the

28

clam from the bottom like a cork from a bottle, and eats it after its own peculiar fashion.

The most obvious suggestion is that the starfish smells the clam. There are, however, a few facts which give food for thought. For one thing, many clams dig themselves into the sand diagonally, and for another, the ground they crawl through has water passing through it, so that it can hardly be assumed that the starfish is tracking down a scent while it digs. Yet so far it has not been possible to suggest any other hypothesis.

In this context a curious observation dating from 1961 may be mentioned. Clams are sensitive to X-rays and radioactive rays, which immediately cause them to shut up their shells and dig themselves down as deep as possible. Further research will show what organs serve these molluscs as 'Geiger counters'.

This last example of course provides no evidence about the secrets of the starfish 'position-finder'. But it shows the surprising possibilities we still have to reckon with in the mysterious senses of animals.

2

NATURE'S INVENTIONS

The Incubator Bird

AT the close of the Middle Ages men still believed in mermaids and other fabulous creatures. But when Gemelli Careri, one of the eighteen survivors of Magellan's voyage round the world between 1519 and 1522, stated that there were birds in Australia that built heated incubators for hatching their eggs, his story was regarded as a sailor's yarn.

Three centuries later, when white settlers in the interior of Australia came on peculiar incubator mounds, which are ten feet in diameter and reach a height of sixteen feet, it was thought that they must be the tombs of aboriginal warriors, or the playgrounds of aboriginal children.

It is only within the last twenty years that Dr. H. J. Frith of the Scientific Research Organisation of Australia has discovered more about this well-nigh incredible bird 'invention'.

At the beginning of the present century superficial observers had assumed that the incubator bird, as a result of its 'brilliant invention', led a comfortable and lazy life, as there was apparently no need for it to attend to the tedious brooding business. But the exact opposite is the case. Long ages ago a caprice of nature placed it in a grotesque predicament, from which it extricated itself and preserved itself from destruction only by an infinitely toilsome and tormenting stratagem.

The bird looks like a small turkey and weighs about three and a half pounds. But its eggs are nearly half the size of an ostrich egg, they weigh as much as half a pound. Moreover, the female lays one of these huge eggs from every four to eight days during the summer, or thirty-five in one season. As with each egg brooding goes on for seven weeks before the chick hatches, the bird has to be hatching from seven to ten eggs weighing altogether up to five pounds – more than its own weight. Obviously it cannot keep such a mountain of eggs warm, so it has had to 'invent'.

The 'fuel' for the incubator consists of damp, rotting grass and leaves, in which myriads of bacteria produce very considerable heat from decomposition. If not given proper attention, this might overheat and result in spontaneous combustion, like excessively damp hay in a barn.

So the incubator bird needs damp foliage and damp grasses. But how is it to get these in the Australian bush, where throughout the summer, while the hatching goes on, practically no rain falls? Dry hay does not rot, and therefore does not produce heat by decomposition. Instead it is eaten by termites, blown away by the wind or burnt by bush fires. If the bird collected the fuel immediately before the brooding period, it would be wasting its time.

Consequently, in the Australian autumn, six months before brooding begins, it takes its first precautions. With its excessively large feet it digs a hole ten feet deep. Then it scratches up leaves and grass from a surrounding area of about 5,000 square yards and stows this away in the hole. The hole is left with a funnel-shaped opening, so that during the winter as much rain-water as possible flows in and keeps the organic matter damp. If it does not rain, the bird abandons its heat store and does not brood next summer. It seems to know that its incubator cannot function without moisture.

A Life of Hard Labour

At the opening of the dry season, shortly before the beginning of spring, the male, who with the prejudice of a misogynist carries out the soil and compost operations alone, returns to his hole. He digs up and turns over the whole fermentation pit several times a day, drawing clouds of hot vapour out of it. In this way he keeps the system well aired, until the superfluous heat has escaped and the right temperature of 91 degrees Fahrenheit (33 degrees Centigrade) has been reached.

Only then does he allow the female to enter the incubator mound, of course only for the short period of egg-laying. For this he opens the structure at one particular spot, a task which takes him an hour or rather longer. At a sign the female, who has been waiting patiently in the bushes close by, comes over and carefully scrutinises the passage dug out and the egg repository provided by her mate.

If she is not satisfied, she goes away again, and sits down under a bush. Then no alternative is left to him but to fill in the hole and dig another. This may be repeated three or four times before she is satisfied. It is touching to watch the male peeping over her shoulder trying to make out whether or not his handiwork meets with her approval.

As soon as the egg is laid, she leaves her lord and master, disappears, and returns only from four to eight days later to lay the next egg.

Meanwhile the male has an absolutely overwhelming task in keeping the egg-chamber of the incubator at the correct temperature. It must not vary by more than one degree if all his labour is not to prove vain.

In the spring the bird visits the mound every morning shortly before dawn, digs himself down as far as the egg-chamber and instals ventilation corridors, enabling the decomposition warmth which is necessary during the night, but superfluous when once solar radiation begins, to escape. Towards evening he stops up the air-holes.

At the beginning of the summer it is no longer simply a matter of airing. The decomposition warmth of the heat base does indeed diminish rapidly as the energy content of the compost is exhausted, but now the blazing sun threatens to overheat the eggs. Because of this the bird from now on covers his incubator with a layer of sand which, as the daytime heat increases, he makes thicker and thicker. Towards midsummer it finally reaches a depth of three feet. This means that this

Greater horseshoe bat in flight. The megaphone-type nose, focusing the ultrasonic sounds that issue from the nostrils, can be easily identified. Head and ears swing from side to side, scanning horizontally for sound echoes and thus providing the animal with a 'pictorial' impression.

An unusual flashlight photograph of a fish-catching bat. It has located its prey (invisible in the picture) and is diving for it.

Dolphins can become good friends and play-fellows of man. Here is the dolphin Suzie being rubbed with sun-tan lotion by Jimmy Kline, a colleague of Dr. Lilly's. Meanwhile a second dolphin is awaiting its turn impatiently. Dr. Lilly believes that dolphins have a complete sound language.

small creature, which – let us repeat – is no bigger than an average size chicken, has to scrape together from round about a total of twenty cubic yards of sand and earth – an almost incredible feat, which is surpassed only by what comes next.

At midsummer the sun's heat in the Australian desert plains is so great that even this thick layer no longer gives adequate protection. But the bird cannot cope with much larger masses of sand. Accordingly he builds into the incubator mound something which may quite well be compared to a refrigerator. Very early in the morning, when a fresh breeze is still blowing,

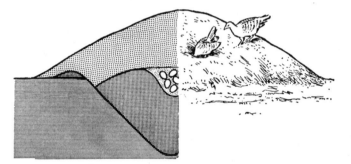

View and cross-section of the heated incubator mound. The male looks over the inspecting female's shoulder to see if she is satisfied with his work.

he sets to work flattening out large quantities of sand beside the mound, so that they may cool over the widest surface possible. Hardly has that been done when, complaining and panting at the never-ending labour, he loads the cool sand through a passage close to the egg-chamber before the first warming rays of sunshine appear.

Every morning the incubator bird unpacks these quantities of cooling sand, spreads them out again over the ground until they are cool enough, and then moves the huge load back into his hole. It is especially worthy of note that he transports neither too much nor too little, but every day exactly the right amount of sand needed to counterbalance precisely the solar heat to be expected in the hours that follow.

In the autumn, when the sun is losing strength and the decay heat of the fuel is nearly used up, the incubator bird is faced with the opposite problem. Now he does not appear at the mound before about 10 a.m., when the sun is already shining on it, and he scrapes away the sand cover until the egg-chamber is just a few inches below the surface and the structure takes on the appearance of a large saucer.

The life-giving midday heat can now penetrate into the structure. This is not sufficient for the night, however, which in the Australian bush is as a rule bitterly cold. So in the noonday hours the bird now spreads out larger quantities of sand, allows them to be warmed in the sun, and then scrapes them – again with enormous physical effort – close to the egg-chamber, this time as a 'stove'. He does not finish this laborious thermodynamic precision work until about 4 p.m.

What is most astonishing is that the bird is not rigid in its routine. If a spring day is exceptionally hot, it behaves as if it were summer. If the weather grows cooler again, it returns to the technique appropriate for spring.

To submit the bird's technical skill to an unusual test, Dr. Frith on a normal spring day carried out 'sabotage' on an incubator mound. In the course of an hour, during which the male had gone searching for food, he removed nearly the whole of the organic fuel from the structure, thus depriving it of its internal source of heat. On its return the bird at once noted the cause of the disturbance and promptly switched to the procedure it is accustomed to use in the autumn only, which in this case was the only sensible one.

In a second experiment Dr. Frith hid in an intact incubator mound three electric heating stoves which were supplied by a 240-volt diesel unit about a hundred yards away. The incubator bird became wildly excited, as if it could not account for the continual alternation between hot and cold. But, by installing ventilation shafts, thickening or reconstituting the sand cover or carrying in cool or hot sand, it always took exactly the right measures to maintain the correct temperature in the egg-chamber. Dr. Frith failed to alter the heat conditions in the structure more rapidly than the bird corrected them.

Thus the bird knows exactly whether too much or too little warmth is being supplied from the heating in the interior of the structure or from solar radiation, and takes the appropriate measures to meet the situation, radically different, complicated and physically exhausting though these are in each case. What it does is fully equivalent to what we humans would call rational work. In particular, the bird has an absolute temperature sense, and can perceive variations in heat of fractions of a degree. While at work it sticks its beak into the mound every few minutes, withdraws it full of sand, and then lets the sample trickle out slowly on both sides after 'tasting' the temperature with the 'thermometer' in its tongue or soft palate.

In spite of this devoted labour, all the eggs are seldom hatched out. Downpours of thundery rain may silt up the mound and drench the interior. Foxes and other beasts of prey are well aware of the tasty contents, dig through the structure and devour many of the eggs.

The lot of the young chicks is very hard too. Their parents are so much taken up with incubation that they cannot look after their offspring after the latter have crept out of the shell. The newly hatched chick's life of labour begins with its having to work its way up unassisted from the egg chamber to the fresh air through all the layers of compost and sand. This laborious journey may take it from fifteen to twenty hours. Not a few of the young creatures fail in the effort, and suffocate on the way.

As soon as the chick has worked its way out of the incubator mound, it staggers or rolls exhausted down the slope, and for a few hours seeks shelter under the nearest bush. As a rule it never sees its parents. After this pause for recovery, however, it is able to run. On the same day, shortly before nightfall, it flies to a bough to sleep. This loneliness in a barren, cruel semi-desert is its lot for the rest of its toilsome life. It flees from everything that moves in the bush, even from members of its own race, with the exception of its mate.

But, when the male chicken has grown up and the brooding period comes, he builds and looks after the complicated incubator just as efficiently as his father did, though he has never seen how it is done.

Living Power Station

It should be stated at the outset that the electric or 'trembling' eel, contrary to assumptions frequently expressed, does not tremble. It only makes others tremble, for instance, a man bathing in the Amazon if he gets too close. The latter then has the extremely unpleasant feeling that he has touched a high tension cable from which he cannot get free, however much he struggles and cries out. Meanwhile the electric eel, making no abnormal movements, remains in a position from which it can best give the intruder electric shocks.

Incidentally, the electric ray, which the Romans called the torpedo, a name adopted by the navy, was used by Roman physicians in Nero's time for electric shock therapy. Of course they had not the slightest idea of the nature of electricity, but believed that the fish lashed at the human body so swiftly that its movement could not be seen, but could be only felt. Nevertheless they used to make their patients go down into a pool with the ray, to cure them of gout, migraine and mental illnesses through shocks from the fish.

For electric eels, electric rays and electric cat-fish (altogether there are about 500 different types of electric fish of which not more than twenty have been at any rate partially investigated), the 'invention' of the internal power station is an effective weapon for stunning or killing prey and for frightening off bigger enemies.

In the fight for a territory or a female the males of many types of electric eel engage in relentless high-tension combat with their rivals. Fish with weaker electric power use it for underwater position-fixing, for navigation, for detecting prey and as an instrument of warning to assailants.

The most impressive, however, is the electric eel, which is up to two and a half yards long and is a river type. Its electrical output is such that it can be used to light twelve forty-watt incandescent lamps simultaneously – though of course only for quite a short time. An electric eel in a domestic aquarium unfortunately cannot be used to effect economies in the electricity bill. Nevertheless, it is a matter of exceptional interest technically to investigate how the electric eel produces powerful electric currents in its body. In all organisms muscles and nerves produce electric potentials which, to be sure, are only very feeble. In the human heart a physician with an electrocardiograph (E.K.G.) can detect a potential of just one-thousandth of a volt. Every pathological change of the heart action is reflected characteristically in the total potential produced by the heart muscles, so that the specialist can diagnose the type of cardiac affection from the course of the E.K.G.-curve recorded. During this examination the patient must lie on a bed completely relaxed, as every movement and exertion of other muscles causes other electric currents and disturbs the heart current curves, making diagnosis impossible. The electric currents of the brain are recorded in like manner in the electro-encephalogram (E.E.G.).

Thus it is not surprising that the body of the electric eel consists up to 40 per cent of a muscle-type tissue – or rather muscle which has no power of contraction but instead has specialised in the production of electric current. Microscopical examination of this muscular tissue discloses a concentration of from one to two million minute 'flash-light batteries', and the electric potential indeed originates in the elements of this tissue, that is, in the individual cells of the electro-organ, in much the same way as in a flash-light battery. The electric cell provides, in a way we still do not understand, for the concentration on the inside of its thin-skinned wall of negatively charged ions and on the outside of positively charged

37

ions. Thus between the interior and the exterior of an electric cell there exists a natural electric potential of about one-tenth of a volt.

So small a voltage, however, is not enough to stun a fish that the electric eel desires for its prey. Nature therefore connects up millions of battery cells exactly as an electrician wires together the many batteries in an electric truck.

To increase the voltage, some 8,000 of these wafer-shaped

Left – The dotted area shows the 'power station' of the electric eel.
Right – What the separate cells of the electro-organ look like under the microscope; batteries of o·1 voltage.

cells, stacked very close together into a pile and parallel with the backbone of the fish, are ranged one after the other, so that their individual potentials build up to a total of 500 volts. To increase the strength of current at the same time, about 140 of such battery piles lie parallel with one another, their combined power amounting to one ampere.

Of course this remarkable output of half a kilowatt cannot come into operation in the quiescent state described so far. For the current actually to flow through the battery piles a 'valve' on each of the millions of electric cells has first to be opened, and they must all be opened simultaneously. The ingenuity of the technique by which the eel accomplishes this was discovered at the end of the fifties by Professor Harry Grundfest, of Columbia University, New York.

The principle sounds rather simple. The wall surface of each wafer-shaped electric cell at the tail end of the fish becomes penetrable by the negatively laden ions concentrated in the cell interior in pulses of a ten-thousandth of a second. All these ions are released like lightning in the direction of the tail and thus produce the electric current.

At first there seemed to be no answer to the question of how the eel was able in such an extremely short time to open and shut a million cell walls for the negative molecules. For this it possesses exceedingly complex nerve controls. Each of the millions of cell walls is permeated by a close network of fine nerve endings which, when they receive an impulse from the eel's brain, release a chemical (acetylcholine), which makes the cell wall penetrable.

A control centre in the brain must give the command, and in such a way that it arrives in all the electric cells simultaneously. This is in reality more complicated than appears at first sight, for the electric signals pass along the nerve cords, which are up to two and a half yards along, at a relatively slow pace. In the absence of supplementary technical measures, the batteries at the tail-end would receive the news later than those near the head. The result would be that the rear cells would not begin to 'spark' till after the front had been discharged. The whole mechanism would get out of time, and the electric action would peter out without having fulfilled its purpose. This example shows that extraordinarily complex technical problems can be tackled by nature with 'engineering' methods.

In order to discharge all the millions of batteries simultaneously in spite of this complication, nature devised two different methods. For one thing, it made the shorter nerve conductors thinner than the longer. In thinner nerves the electric impulses pass more slowly than in the thicker, so that the difference in distance is nearly cancelled out by the time delay. Only nearly, however. As the connexion as a whole must work precisely to a thousandth of a second, this correction does not suffice. So, as Professor Grundfest found out, in the shorter nerve conductors 'waiting rooms' for electric impulse signals are installed, which in a very complicated way delay the electric impulses until identical signals have alerted even the hindmost tail battery. Modern electronic calculating machines also have such delayed action units.

That is the fantastic fashion in which the dreaded current

impulses arise, up to 1,500 of which electric fish can discharge in a second. Moreover, each species of electric fish has its own individual series of volleys, which it always keeps so exactly constant that high-grade laboratory oscillographs alone can compete with their stability of oscillation. Only when an ice-bag is strapped round the head of an electric eel do the incessant volleys of electric discharges slow down.

A further question presents itself – how it is that the electric eel does not electrocute itself on its own 'electric chair'. An engineer could not have worked to a better design. All the electric cells are connected in such a way that the current can flow only through them and cannot deviate to other parts of the body.

At the two places in the outer skin at which the electric current leaves and re-enters the fish's body there is only a filmy membrane. The rest of the skin consists of a thick insulating integument with which the animal protects itself from itself.

Flies Have a Speedometer

Now and then scientists investigating animal anatomy dis-cover curious sense organs whose purpose they cannot at once detect. That was the case in 1957 at the zoological institute of Würzburg University, where two neurophysiologists, Dr. Dietrich Burkhardt and Dr. Günter Schneider, were working on that commonplace creature, the bluebottle.

It was known that in many insects a small number of sensory nerve cells are to be found in the two joints that connect the antennae with the head. Their purpose was unknown. The true sensory nerve cells with which the fly smells and feels are actually in the antennae, and there are thousands of them. What, in face of this multiplicity, was the meaning of these three or four nerve cells inside the antenna joint?

The two scientists carried out an experiment. They bound up a bluebottle with a special 'belt' and took it like an aircraft into a small wind-tunnel. Beforehand they had tapped with microscopically small needles the single sensory nerve cells in the antenna joint, to intercept the nerve signals sent from there to the fly's brain. The electric nerve monitoring device resembled in its main features the appliance described above with which the bat alarm was discovered in the 'ears' of moths.

With 'wind force nil' complete 'radio silence' prevailed in the antenna nerves of the fly. But, as soon as a light wind passed gently over the insect, the sensory nerve cells began to transmit impulses at regular intervals. With increasing air speed there was a steady increase in the speed of transmission.

The bluebottle thus has in its antenna joints a highly efficient wind speed indicator. The air stream presses the two antennae backwards against the muscular tension. This tilt is noted by the sensory nerve cells in the antenna joint and converted into a corresponding series of volleys of the nerve signals.

The next experiment confirmed this finding. On a windless day the scientists with a pair of tweezers pressed back the fly's two antennae as if they were small levers. The sensory nerve cells telegraphed exactly the same signals to the fly's brain as if the slanting position of the antennae had been caused by the wind. The fly's reactions too were the same. It placed its wings in the flight attitude – one might say 'it retracted its undercarriage' – and, according to how far back the antennae were pressed, it changed the figure of eight described by its wing-tips during pulsation and the angle of incidence in the wings – both being measures taken by the fly to alter the speed of flight.

This confirmed the hypothesis that the insect uses its windspeed indicator as a 'tachometer' for determining its speed of flight – a conclusion which is not so obvious as it appears, for there are a number of insects that have a different use for it.

For the purpose of seeing how the 'tachometer' operates in practice, the fly's antennae were pressed back and fastened firmly in that position; then in the laboratory the insect was made to fly over a 'race track'. At this point the two scientists established the fact that the farther back the fly's antennae were bent, the more slowly it flew. The electric nerve signals were thus reporting to the fly's brain a falsified speed of flight. The animal thought it was flying too fast and arranged its wing-beat in such a way that its flight was slowed down.

By chance the two scientists were presented with a further discovery. During one of these experiments, in which the sensory nerve cells of the fly were tapped for interception, a colleague suddenly burst into the laboratory and began talking loudly, whereupon the cells sent impulses to the fly's brain, although it was still absolutely calm and the antennae were at rest. The nervous system of the bluebottle therefore reacted to sound waves. Is it possible that a bluebottle can hear? Does its behaviour indicate a reaction to human words? No. The insect did not fly away when it was shouted at. Its own flight sound, which was played over to it on a tape, impressed it just as little as the rather different flight sound of its mate. Even echoes of its own noise, which were reverberated from a wall and might have done service for orientation when flying in the dark, did not interest it. So why the fly can actually 'hear' is still a puzzle. Presumably its speed indicator is so sensitive that it responds to the air vibrations caused by sound. Yet the fly's brain is obviously not equipped for 'understanding', manipulating and converting into reactions in behaviour the irregular 'Morse signals' it receives in sound.

The 'Joy-stick' of the Dung-beetle

The same impulses from the sensory nerve cells in the antenna joint, which in the bluebottle cause the figure of eight in the wing beat, the angle of incidence in the wings and the setting of the legs, produce different effects in other insects. One example is the dung-beetle, a creature which is socially quite acceptable in zoological circles. This long-legged animal does not 'hold the road' well and is markedly sensitive to cross-winds. It therefore does not use the anemometer in its antenna joints for determining its speed of locomotion. A 'tachometer' would be rather uninteresting to it. It uses this 'invention' simply as a wind-force and wind-direction indicator. Professor Georg Birukow discovered this in a series of interesting experiments at the zoological institute of the University of Freiburg in Breisgau in 1958. If the wind is directed over the beetle from the front, it bows its head forward; if the wind comes from behind, it raises it high. In a cross-wind it tilts round its longitudinal axis and with its smooth back leans against the wind as if it had a 'list'. The greater the force of the wind, the more pronounced and vigorous are the attitudes it adopts to offer minimum resistance to it and improve the pull of its legs.

Like the bluebottle, the dung-beetle can be deluded into accepting any wind force and any wind direction if its antennae are artificially deflected with a pair of tweezers. It is curious to watch this. As soon as the 'joy-stick' of the dung-beetle antenna is bent to the right, the whole animal throws itself to the left, if the 'lever' is pressed backward, it bucks forward.

Here we have a very clear example of the fact that stimulation of a similar sense organ in two such different creatures as the bluebottle and the dung-beetle can cause two distinct types of behaviour. This shows how intimately the behaviour of animals is associated with the inherited structure of their nervous system.

The Bee Without its Hinder Half

Among the 'inventions' in the animal kingdom that are most enviable to man is the ability of some reptiles and amphibians, for instance lizards, salamanders and newts, to replace completely, to regenerate, lost parts of the body. This is far from applying only to the tail, which can be parted with if a pursuer has taken hold of it. A common pond newt can grow new legs of full size and perfection any number of times if they are seized and eaten by a predatory fish. In this context we may be reminded of the experiments carried out in the eighteenth century by the great Italian naturalist Spallanzani.

43

When he repeatedly cut off the same leg it always quickly grew again, complete with thigh, tibia, fibula, tarsal bones, toe bones and joints. In six months one single animal grew 1,374 new bones in this way. This amphibian can similarly replace its eyes, complete with cornea and lens, if they are pecked out by a bird.

Among the most exciting scientific work taking place today is research into what goes on in the body of newts when they grow new limbs or eyes.

Are special hormones involved in the process? Does the primary growth of nerve circuits give the decisive impulse, or do yet other causes exist?

These studies are in full swing in several countries, and the hope seems not entirely unjustified that one day it will prove possible to provide the injured with the capacity to replace an amputated leg, a lost arm or a blinded eye.

Just as some lizards can save their lives by sacrificing their tail, so many insects can automatically part with a limb when a marauder takes hold of it. In view of the wholesale massacre that takes place in the insect realm, this capacity, together with the surprising fact that the insects do not feel pain in losing parts of their body, but survive and can produce offspring, is an 'invention' not to be underrated in the struggle for existence.

One very extreme case was observed by Professor Karl von Frisch, the Nestor of bee research of the zoological institute of Munich University, now retired. One day, after a rather long absence, he returned to the experiment table in his garden to see a bee licking a honey-pot suddenly attacked from behind by a wolf-spider. It lost the whole back part of its body. Practically speaking, only the front half of the insect was left. But this half, contrary to expectation, was as much alive as ever and went on sucking in honey without pause, though the honey poured out again at the severed waist.

Obviously the bee felt no pain. Indeed, it behaved exactly as if it had not lost its hinder part at all. The bee's brain merely did not now receive the 'I have had enough' signal —

44

which would have put a stop to its endless voracity. That it lived for only a few hours longer goes without saying.

Radical mutilation such as in this instance was brought about by chance is routine among a certain type of southern European praying mantis. The female of this bellicose predatory species at the beginning of the nuptials pounces on the courting male, who is somewhat smaller and weaker, holds him with her muscular forelegs in an iron embrace, and during the nuptial act devours the front two-thirds of him, beginning with the head. Thanks to the independence of the reflex life, the remainder of the male is able to continue fulfilling its biological function.

It can hardly be said that there is any sense in this curious behaviour. The bridegroom as the wedding dish of the praying mantis indeed serves to strengthen — as occurs too, in the case of many types of spider — the constitution of the female. But she could just as well nourish herself on other species. Certainly no compelling necessity exists for this horrifying practice.

It is accounted for by something else. This is an unusual example of a very voracious and aggressive predator in whom the instinct of restraint on eating its own kind or mating partner does not function. But this does not work against the preservation of the species, because the male, once copulation has taken place, has fulfilled his function and serves no further purpose. Higher species would long ago have brought about their own extinction by such behaviour.

3
SECRET WEAPONS AND STRATAGEMS

Bomb-sight of the Glow-worm

THE mating of the glow-worm is accompanied by very special rites. On warm summer evenings the females of this Cantharidae species climb up on tall blades of grass, stones or tree-stumps and cause the luminous organs on the under-side of their hinder part to let forth a greenish glow. So that it shall be visible from afar as a directional lighthouse and an 'I am still free' signal to males eager for wedlock, they bend back their hinder half until the 'luminous plaque' of the under-side points upward.

A female glow-worm has raised its back and emits a fluorescent light to entice a male.

Meanwhile the males circle round in a slow questing flight from about three to six feet above ground-level. If one of the suitors – and they are very fastidious – discovers a female whose luminosity is particularly attractive, he approaches her like a bomber, and at the moment of release drops on her with wings laid flat.

For this manoeuvre he possesses an accurate 'bomb-sight'.

Even a trifling deviation from the target would involve the enamoured insect in a fatiguing crawl, if indeed it did not plump him so far down that he could not see the female overhead.

To test the accuracy of aim of these bombardiers, Professor Friedrich Schaller, of the zoological department of the Braunschweig Institute of Technology, arranged some practice for them. The target was a luminous female on the floor of a glass vessel open on top and, to make the conditions more difficult, six inches high and an inch and a quarter in diameter.

The result surpassed expectations. No fewer than 65 of 100 males obtained direct hits. In the open air it was frequently observed that males dropped on the luminous female with an audible smack. The less good bombardiers landed just beside the target and at once tried to reach the beloved on foot.

Incidentally, the brighter and 'more beautiful' the luminosity of a female, the better are its chances in courtship. Older females in their latter days can considerably increase their chances by waggling their luminous posterior.

If a male has literally made a hit with a female, her lamp promptly goes out, and a mass onset of 'husbands' is thus avoided. The illumination must already have roused the male's ardour, but if his bride switched off too soon he might easily glimpse another even more alluring female, and leave her in the lurch. For with glow-worms love expires with the lamp.

Gas Warfare

Another good marksman is the bombardier-beetle. When pursued by an enemy it discharges at it a pungently-smelling cloud of vapour, accompanied by an audible report. If need be, this long-legged ground-beetle, which lives under sun-baked stones, can do this up to twenty times in succession.

Generally it does not need to expend itself in this manner, for its aim is surprisingly good at distances up to twenty inches. Most assailants when gassed in this way are dazed and renounce the prospect of a meal.

Contrary to earlier assumptions, the bombardier-beetle does not use an 'air gun' with compressed air from the intestines, but a high explosive rocket fuel which it produces in two glands. Immediately before the shot two separately produced chemicals, hydroquinone and hydrogen peroxide, pass through a muscular valve to the 'rocket combustion chamber', which has armour-plating of hard chitin. Here the rocket explodes.

Biochemists have now gone to school to the bombardier-beetle to discover the secrets of its highly effective explosion chemistry. So far they have not had much success. Whenever they mix the two chemical substances an explosion takes place. How the animals manage to set fire to the explosive mixture only when they want to is still their secret. Astronauts of the future have probably much to learn from them.

Gas warfare is also conducted by the scorpion-spider *Mastigoproctus giganteus*. Instead of a poisonous sting it has another dangerous weapon. It has acid glands from which it can spray an insidious poison on its target from a distance of up to sixteen inches. Ants, spiders, jays and other birds which, in general, like to eat scorpions take flight at the mere sight of the creature. If they are hit by the poison they are disabled and take quite a time to recover. On human skin the poison causes acute pain; on the mucous membranes in mouth, nose and eyes it is intolerable.

The scorpion-spider almost seems to know about these things, for if a big, thick-skinned, or even an armoured foe such as the armadillo, to which it can do no harm, approaches, it refrains from shooting at it. Instead it sprays its own body with the poison to make itself unpalatable. No sooner does its voracious enemy touch it with mouth or nose than a stabbing pain causes it to turn away.

The secret of the poison lies in the recipe; 5 per cent norleucine is included to open the pores of the skin to obtain swift entry for the real poison, the highly corrosive acetic acid.

Duel with Cupid's Darts

The harmless-looking edible snail is equipped with a not entirely harmless shooting and stinging weapon. There is a glandular chamber in the soft mass of its body just behind the eyes. After each shot it can within a week produce a new sharp dart a centimetre in length by excreting carbonate of lime in it. At the base of the projector a feed line opens, through which a propellant is introduced shortly before the shot. This built-in 'gun' is not used for hunting. Instead it resembles an example in real life of something from classical

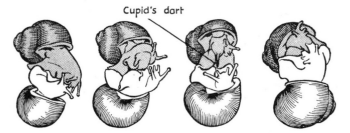

Cupid's dart

Two Roman snails duelling with Cupid's darts. The four drawings show different phases which occur at approximately half-hourly intervals. In the third picture the black Cupid's dart can be identified; in the fourth, copulation ensues.

mythology – Cupid's dart. If a scientific worker wishes to observe the mating of these creatures he needs almost infinite patience. When two of these hermaphrodites – they are both male and female in one – meet, they circle round each other at a snail's pace. Finally they rise and put head against head as if they were going to crawl up on each other, press sole against sole and feel around each other in an almost endless to-and-fro.

After this violent exertion each takes a breather of about a quarter of an hour. Each animal as a rule pauses at a different moment, so that they fail to achieve harmony.

They therefore make preparations to bombard each other with their Cupid's darts. Yet although both animals, upright with sole against sole, adhere firmly to each other and only need to hit their opposite number anywhere on the body they like, the duel may last up to two hours.

The first to fire its dart, which it does with a slight hiss, feels a desire again to take a prolonged break, but the other only twitches in a brief spasm of pain and gives it no peace. Ultimately synchronisation is achieved with the aid of Cupid's darts, and this leads to the object of the whole operation.

It is not yet known whether the stimulating effect of the Cupid's dart is due to the mechanical contact or whether carbonate of lime serves as a 'love potion'. The dart may cause dangerous injury to the intestinal cavity or other internal organ of a snail that is struck. As a rule, however, it strikes the hard, slimy foot or its edges and penetrates only about a millimetre.

Shooting Down Flies

In the mangrove belt of river mouths and small bays in south-east Asia and Northern Australia there lives the archerfish, which shoots down flies and other insects with the proficiency of an artilleryman, and then eats them.

The fish, about the length of a finger, swims just below the surface and stalks an insect resting and sunning itself unsuspectingly on a water plant. When within ten inches it begins taking aim. Professor Hediger, director of the Zoological Gardens in Zürich, has observed it in action.

The fish cocks its whole body at the insect like a gun-barrel, taking care, however, not to penetrate the surface and so scare it. It prefers firing vertically, and dislikes oblique angles of fire for three reasons. For one thing, ballistics, the calculation of the so-called angle of elevation, causes it certain difficulties. For another, the light is refracted on the surface and falsifies the direction of the target, and thirdly, the prey when shot does not drop straight into its open mouth.

To eliminate minor errors of marksmanship, the shot, a fine jet of water ejected from the mouth, is fired fanwise and thus covers a larger target area. The fish thus secures a direct hit almost every other time. In case it fires wide or the insect holds on, it can fire up to seven times in quick succession.

Further efforts would be useless for, as soon as fish of its own kind notice that one of them is shooting, they hasten to try and snatch the prey from in front of the marksman's nose.

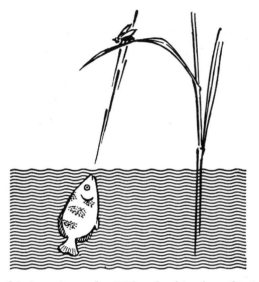

The archer-fish shoots down a fly. Without breaking the surface it takes aim with its whole body and spits out a fan-shaped jet of water.

That is far from being the last in the range of wonder weapons for attack or defence against considerably stronger foes. The caterpillar of the Harpya-spinner, for example, which is akin to the silkworm, is able to drive off numbers of its antagonists with an extendible weapon. It has two horns, not on its head, but on its 'stern'. If it is pursued by ants or other predators, it begins by taking to flight, turning its horned hinder part towards the enemy.

When the predator approaches within about an inch and a quarter, two whip filaments of considerable length spring out of the horns, like automatically extendible telescope antennae, and lash out wildly in all directions.

Most assailants take to flight after being hit once or twice.

These whips, like all the other weapons of defence in the animal kingdom, obviously offer no absolute protection. They can ward off this or that preying enemy, but not all. Even so, in view of the holocausts that take place in the insect world, an improvement of the survival quota of only a few per cent may be decisive for the survival of the species. This is plainly demonstrated by an extremely long-legged fly species from the tropics. When it sits on a branch and perceives the approach of an enemy, it stamps about on the spot at such a furious speed that its whole body vibrates and it vanishes from human sight, like a rotating aircraft propeller.

No doubt it similarly disappears from the sight of many an animal foe. But its most dangerous enemy, a predatory wasp, according to the latest investigation, has optic nerves which are not so lazy as those of man. It is able to see the fly under its magic hood of vibration as plainly as we see a trotting horse.

Nylon Fabric in the Primeval Forest

No less curious are the prey-catching weapons of some kinds of spider. The web of the Nephila silkworm in Madagascar measures a square yard. The thread spun by the animal is so strong that the natives fashion it into textiles.

The girls collect well-nourished female spiders from webs in the primeval forest, clamp them in holders at home and wind the threads out of the spinning glands. Spiders 'milked empty' are put out again on their old webs, to be used afresh three days later as 'nylon' purveyors. The materials woven from these spun fibres are said to glisten like gold and to be more durable and lighter than silk.

The web-throwing spider lives in South Africa. In the daytime it remains in a state of death-like torpor and can be distinguished from a bud on the branch only with great difficulty. At nightfall, when its most dangerous enemies have gone to sleep, it weaves a web the size of a postage stamp from rubber-like fibres and puts it between its legs.

If a moth or a fly comes buzzing along, the spider with its long legs stretches the web to six times its original size and throws it dextrously over the insect in flight, thus immobilising it and wrapping it up ready for eating.

Spider v. Wasp

The Australian lasso-throwing spider is content with a single spinning thread. It weights the thread with a drop of glue at one end. The other it holds firm with one leg, and while lying in wait keeps this weapon whirling in a circle, to take unerring aim when prey comes within range. If the victim is struck only on a wing-tip, it is caught fast and is done for.

One of the most enthralling features of the animal kingdom is the warfare between spiders and their arch-enemies, the predatory wasps. These wasps immobilise their victims with a well-aimed sting in a nerve ganglion. This puts the spider's legs and jaw-pincers out of action, and then the wasp buries it. Though maimed, it survives for a long time, and the wasp uses it as a meat store for its offspring, keeping it in an earth pit dug for the purpose.

Even the notorious bird-spider of the tropics, whose body is three and a half inches long, is not safe from the wasp, which is nearly always considerably smaller than its prey, and it is often a real labour of Hercules for the winged predator to drag a gigantic lump of meat like a maimed spider over grasses and stones to the prepared hole.

During the struggle between them, which has gone on for millions of years, both spider and wasp have constantly developed new methods and weapons and counter-weapons of ever greater subtlety. In the evolution of these animals nature has constantly produced new inventions, improving the combative technique and stratagems of both parties in attack and defence.

In the simplest case the wasp swoops down like a fighter on the spider sitting in the middle of its web. Different kinds of spiders take different defence measures against this kind of attack. Some avoid the middle of the web, hide under leaves at its edge or construct a more or less ingenious hiding-place.

Others stretch alarm lines near the web. They are laid in such a way that an approaching wasp cannot fail to touch them. The split-second delay is sufficient to allow the spider to take evasive action and drop to safety in the abyss below.

Another kind of spider, when a buzzing wasp approaches, vibrates itself and the web so as to become 'invisible', just like the fly described above. Some tropical spiders weave into their web a number of dummies which look exactly like themselves. There is always the chance that the wasp will attack a dummy, thus allowing the spider to escape before the wasp discovers its error. To escape, the spider drops down as swift as lightning on an Ariadne thread and hides under foliage or in a hole in the ground. But some predatory wasps have 'learnt' to follow the fall-thread, without which the spider cannot find its way back to the web, and thus very quickly track down the hiding-place of their victims.

The spiders safest from wasps are those that build themselves a thimble-shaped hiding-place at the edge of the web. This conceals them completely, but it delivers them helplessly into the hands of other enemies, the spider-eating spiders, These creep cautiously up to the web of their victim without giving the slightest shock to the swaying support. Once in a good position, they tug at the web with one leg. The spider waiting in its hiding-place — in spite of its eight eyes it is unable to discern sharply outlined objects even at a distance of a few inches — thinks something is caught in the web and hastens blindly towards the fatal bite.

Trap-doors and Trip-wires

Other spiders protect themselves against predatory wasps by digging themselves holes in the ground. Over the entrance hole they set up a trap-door through which insects that crawl that way come tumbling down. Other 'mining spiders' lie in wait at the entrance for prey scurrying past, or stretch trip-wires in all directions to warn them of the presence of prey.

Many predatory wasps do not venture into these ground nests, and with good reason, for in the dark the spider would probably kill them. So they wait in front of the hole, like lurking cats. When the spider timorously feels its way up, hoping that the coast is clear again, the wasp seizes its fore-legs, swings it out in a high arc and stings it.

Other ground-spiders provide their nest with a second exit from which they can observe what the wasp is doing at the first. But this trick does not work against the type of predatory wasp that is prepared for it. This creature inserts its hinder part a short way into the first hole and then hurries to the second hole, where it catches the spider. If this fails the first time, the wasp repeats the manoeuvre until it succeeds.

The defence of many kinds of spider consists of a firmly shuttered hole or nest with doors ingeniously camouflaged and carefully concealed by plants. The doors turn on hinges and can be securely fastened with specially woven guy ropes.

But even this does not completely outwit the wasps. A species whose habitat is Corsica has a very flat head, which enables it to force itself in between door and hinge, and it has developed powerful nippers for cutting through the holding threads. A wasp of this species is not afraid of creeping into the spider's nest to dispatch its victim there.

This does not exhaust the spider's defensive measures. *Nemesia fagei* shuts its nest with a wedge-shaped plug of its own making; the wasps have not so far invented a 'corkscrew' to withdraw it. The bird spider *Rhytidicolus structor* builds a small earth labyrinth. The entrance hole leads into a large compart-ment from which several hinged doors each lead to a side-chamber. If a predatory wasp penetrates the labyrinth, the spider hides in one of the chambers and watches through a door slit, using nooses and trip-wires to see in which chamber the wasp is looking for it. At the right moment it dashes out

55

and immures the wasp in this chamber. When the wasp suffocates or dies of hunger, the spider eats it.

Warfare in the Digestive Calyx

A curious form of warfare takes place in the digestive calyces of carnivorous plants. Some leaves of the Malayan *Nepenthes* form a pitcher protected by a half-turned-down lid against the penetration of rain-water and foreign bodies. The inside wall of the pitcher simultaneously produces three diabolical substances. At the upper edge, which is coloured like a flower, there is a kind of nectar to entice insects.

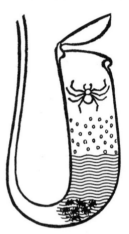

The leaf-pitcher of the carnivorous *Nepenthes gracilis* (pitcher-plant).
Above – A spider living in this 'home'.
Below – At the bottom of the digestive pool the empty chitinous integuments of captured insects.

Directly below it there is slippery wax, on which inquisitive visitors lose their foothold and then fall into the interior of the pitcher; and in the lower part there is a kind of gastric juice, an enzyme which (except for their chitinous coat of mail) resolves into nutrient food the insects that fall into this small digestive lake.

Nevertheless, many animals have chosen this death-trap to live in. Some tropical fly or gnat larvae, and even spiders, have in their body a chemical hormone, an enzyme that decomposes the different enzymes in the digestive juices of the carnivorous plant and makes them harmless as soon as they penetrate through the chitinous coat of mail into their body. Thanks to this property, this dangerous abode becomes the safest place in the world for its occupants, indeed a land of milk and honey, in which other insects, defenceless and half pre-digested, are supplied direct to their chewing jaws. In this way the carnivorous plant is defrauded by its 'sub-tenants', and without return of productive substances useful to its own growth and flower formation.

One type of spider living in these calyces impatiently awaits its victims at the upper edge of the leaf-pitcher and catches every insect enticed by the scent of the false nectar. It looks on the deeper regions of the leaf calyx simply as a safe refuge in emergency.

Emergency generally appears in the form of a predatory wasp. The spider quickly lets itself down on its escape thread. The wasp foolhardily penetrates into the calyx by similarly letting itself down on the thread. The spider then descends to the bottom of the pool of digestive juices and hides there between the hollow chitinous coats of mail of the insects it has devoured. If in a blind fury of aggression the wasp tries to follow it there, in a few seconds the spider's fate is sealed.

The Kiss of Death

The scene of action is a tropical savannah with fields of bamboo, stretching up the slopes of a volcano on the island of Java. About half-way up a bamboo cane an ant is crawling. It has just discovered a bug which it considers excellent prey. It has no suspicion that it belongs to the dangerous family of assassin bugs. Cautiously its goes back to its nest, and in doing so lets its abdomen drag on the ground. The point of the abdomen now operates like a fountain pen, but the stroke it draws is an invisible scent trail. This has a rousing effect on its fellows in the nest, and in a short while ten ants are following the trail to the bug. In face of this superior force by which all way of escape appears to be cut off, things look bad for the bug which, however, resorts to a murderous ruse. Quickly it exudes from its abdominal gland a sweetish, palatable fluid, lets it drip copiously on the bamboo stalk and girdle it around, and withdraws to higher regions.

Scarcely have the ants reached the sweet fluid than they begin greedily sucking it in, forgetting their previous objective. They go on sucking until, drunk and half paralysed, they drop to the ground. The delicious fluid contained a quick-acting poison.

The bug waits calmly until the last ant drops. Then it descends and devours its helpless enemies one after another. In so doing it swallows its own poison, to which, strange to say, it is immune.

The killer bug (or assassin bug, as it is called in the United States) is often attacked by a single ant, and in that event uses different tactics. It takes a drop of its home-produced bait in both forelegs and offers it to the ant, which munches it so greedily that it does not notice the bug's forelegs slowly encircling its neck. The ant could still slay its foe with one bite, but in its intoxication misses the chance. Soon afterwards it is paralysed by the poison, and the bug's double, razor-sharp saw nose bores through its armour. A quick-acting digestive substance is now injected and in a few seconds liquefies all the soft parts contained in the chitin, which the bug then sucks out.

Because of the marked delicacy of feeling that characterises this behaviour, zoologists call it the kiss of death.

4
DUELLING ACCORDING TO
RULE

Snakes' Wrestling Bout

A POWERFUL male rattlesnake invades the preserve of another, to challenge its right to its living-space and its mate. The victim of this aggressive behaviour responds by shooting out its tongue and rattling its horney-scaled tail in a threatening way, and creeps up on the intruder.

Evidently a dangerous situation is developing. A struggle to the death seems inevitable. One single bite or scratch with the venomous tooth might be fatal, for many snakes are very sensitive to their own poison. They eat their prey only when decomposition has made it harmless.

Biting would obviously be the quickest and most effective way of eliminating the rival, in spite of the risk attached, and short shrift would obviously be given to a challenger of any other species, but against an enemy of their own kind no attempt is made to use their deadly teeth. Instead they start a wrestling match in accordance with strict rules. They begin by gliding round each other in diminishing spirals until they lie parallel, head to head. Then, with a half or whole convolution, the hinder third parts of their bodies clasp each other, and simultaneously they rear their front parts to a height of about twenty inches.

At first sight the initial stage of the combat seems very affectionate, with the two reptiles pressing cheek to cheek, but then the observer notices the pressure that lies behind the 'caress'. Both combatants fill their lungs with air and press with all their strength, until they suddenly break away. Their

59

bodies jerk apart like steel springs, and they beat them hard on the ground.

The object is to rise again as quickly as possible and resume the effort to press the other snake sideways. After several such rounds, one of the two combatants manages to exert enough pressure just behind its opponent's head to force it to the ground, where it holds it fast for several seconds. Then it relaxes its hold and allows the loser to escape. The latter makes off without further ado.

Wrestling-match between rattlesnakes.
Left – The heads of the two have just slipped apart and are striking downwards under the pressure of the spring-taut bodies.
Right – The victor presses the head of the vanquished to the ground.

Had not these 'Queensberry rules' for settling differences within the species been worked out among rattlesnakes or their ancestors in remote antiquity, they would hardly survive today. For if they used their real weapons, the result would almost certainly be death for both.

Many other venomous snakes settle their differences in just as gentlemanly a fashion for similar reasons. The common viper, for instance, follows very similar rules, but does not use the 'headlock'; it contents itself with sideways pressure, breaking away, and renewing the pressure, and the trial of strength continues until one of the combatants realises it is beaten and makes off.

Poisonous snakes are not the only creatures that engage in bloodless duels in which not the slightest physical damage is done to either party. Many other animals engage in them too. The more dangerous their weapons, the more scrupulous are the rules.

There is a fundamental resemblance between them all. The two rivals begin by slowly approaching and looking each other over. They try to inflate themselves and look as impressive as possible, making threatening ritual gestures to encourage themselves and intimidate their opponent.

In some cases the duel goes no further than this. The weaker party acknowledges defeat and retires. Pigeons, for instance, duel by swaggering with breast puffed out, strutting about and spreading their plumage. The party that makes the most impressive display is the winner.

The howling monkeys of South America also generally content themselves with empty threats, trying to shout each other down. In the primeval forests the horrible concerts of these vocal contests morning and evening can be heard for miles around.

An especially impressive type of imposing behaviour has been developed by the hippopotamus. Two of these creatures will stand head to head, open their huge mouths as wide as possible, and angrily belch evil-smelling gases in each other's face.

If threats fail to lead to a decision, the duel may be carried a stage further. A fine example is provided by the fallow deer. The two rivals march along for some distance side by side, with head and antlers raised majestically, watching each other all the time out of the corner of their eye.

Suddenly, as if at a word of command, they stop and turn inwards, face each other, mouth to mouth, bow their heads and attack. But they make no attempt to injure each other with the points of their antlers, which they use only to interlock with each other and wrestle with, pushing each other this way and that.

If the first round brings no decision, the marching side by side, the moving into position and the wrestling are repeated in rounds of roughly the same length, until one of the two realises his inferiority and makes off during the 'parade' march.

Sometimes, out of sheer excitement, one of the two animals may turn the wrong way out of the 'parade' march, thus ex-

Duel between two male oryx antelopes. They cross their antlers like foils without hurting each other.

posing its very vulnerable hindquarters to its opponent. The latter, however, never takes advantage of the opportunity, but waits to attack until the other is ready.

Oryx antelopes, whose long horns, sharp as daggers, have gored and killed many a beast of prey, never use this dangerous weapon against their own kind. Instead of thrusting with them, they use them in duelling rather like theatrical sabres, clashing them loudly and furiously on each other.

A strange duel was observed by Dr. Fritz Walther in the Opel deer forest at Kronberg, Germany. A hornless oryx bull quarrelled with a fully-horned rival, and the duel was conducted exactly as if it had horns. It stopped at just the distance that would have allowed its horns to clash against those of its opponent if it had still had them. Its opponent similarly made allowances for the non-existent horns, and parried the imaginary blows delivered with them. Eventually the duel ended indecisively, in a draw.

Capitulation Dance

Curious rules govern the duelling of the Central European sand-lizard *Lacerta agilis*, which is about ten inches long. As Dr. Gertraut Kitzler has observed, after the introductory display of threats one male grasps and bites his rival in the neck, vigorously but without drawing blood, and holds him fast for a while in this unpleasant position. The latter waits patiently and without struggling until the grip is relaxed. Then the other takes his turn to have a bite, and so the contest goes on, until one or other has had enough and gives in. Strange to relate, defeat is generally acknowledged, not after being bitten, but after biting. It is evidently not by its power to bite that this reptile establishes its superiority — since this is carefully kept within bounds to avoid inflicting injury — but by its capacity to tolerate the bite. If the defeated party in a family squabble really fled, it would have a disruptive effect on the social unit on which the life of the sand-lizard depends. It therefore carries out only a symbolic flight. It turns its tail on the victor and dances up and down on the spot for a while. This is accepted as a sign of capitulation, for hostilities are promptly suspended.

War of Nerves by Tree-shrews

An entirely different picture is presented by the duelling of two male tree-shrews. If a male intrudes in another's domain, the occupant bombards him with shrill staccato squeaks. This is generally sufficient to make him withdraw immediately. If he is not quick about it, the master of the domain bites his tail hard and lets himself be dragged to the boundary of his domain by the escaping shrew. If, however, the intruder has more fighting spirit, the two squeak at each other, stand on their hind legs and belabour each other with their forelegs. Occasional harmless bites add a certain zest to the fray. If this fails to decide the issue, extreme measures are taken. One of the two flings himself down on his back and begins to squeak louder than ever. This goes on until his opponent acknowledges his acoustic defeat by running away.

This type of war of nerves is evidently far more disagreeable to tree-shrews than one would suppose. Two American zoologists made a tape-recording of the frantic squeaking and played it back to the little insectivores at a higher volume. It promptly caused them violent convulsions.

Mammals can actually be killed by the noise of jet engines. In the spring of 1962, voles that had become a pest at the Braunschweig-Waggum airfield were nearly all killed within a few weeks of the stationing there of four jet helicopters. The former boxer Max Schmeling had to look on helplessly in 1956 when a military airfield near his mink farm was occupied by jet aircraft and the valuable animals died.

Duelling among rats begins by following the tree-shrew pattern. The rivals bare and grind their teeth, arch their backs, turn imposingly broadside on to each other and utter shrill cries. Then they stand on their hind legs, box and wrestle, and sometimes kick with their hind legs. This goes on until one falls down backwards. That is the end of the contest. The rat lying on its back gives up and runs away. But, according to researches by Dr. Irenäus Eibl-Eibesfeldt of the Max Planck Institute for the Physiology of Behaviour, there is yet another type of rat combat which is in real earnest.

If two rats belonging to different groups come to blows, the beaten animal often refuses to acknowledge defeat and breaks the rules by biting. That is the end of the Queensberry rules, so far as they are concerned. They begin biting furiously, and the battle often ends with the death of one of the combatants.

64

Praying mantis devours her mate.

A predatory wasp attacking a spider. The situation looks very dangerous for the little wasp but that is an illusion. At the right moment it will penetrate a gap between the spider' legs and deal it a paralysing sting.

Thus they can indeed kill their own kind, but in general do not, for as long as their opponent adheres to the duelling rules they are inhibited from using their teeth. It is not that they do not want to destroy the enemy; they cannot, because certain fixed modes of behaviour are innate in them.

Boxing-match between two rats. Now and then the animals kick out, each trying to overthrow the other. The one that loses its balance is the loser.

A defeated dog or wolf averts its head, presenting its throat to the victor in such a way that the latter could kill it with a bite. It is evident that the victor would gladly take advantage of the opportunity, did a mechanism not come into play that prevented it from doing so. It dallies for a few moments, and then moves away, sparing its victim. This strikes us as very magnanimous. But such impulses are totally alien to animals. This analogous-to-moral behaviour is firmly anchored in the mechanism of their inherited instincts. The signal by which the loser acknowledges defeat automatically applies the brake to the winner's aggression, and makes him abide by the rules. But any departure from them shifts the points, as it were, from the act of reprieve to unlimited aggression, generally with fatal results.

The Signal for Capitulation

The signal for capitulation differs with every species. It may be flight, as in the case of the adder and the fallow-deer, or symbolic flight, as in the sand-lizard family.

If monkeys, rats, hamsters and other animals who surrender

by taking to flight are deprived of the possibility of doing so by being confined in a small cage offering no hiding-places with a number of their kind who are strangers to them, they kill each other off ruthlessly. This has often led to trouble when animals have been sent overseas. The cause lay, not in the creatures' 'diabolical instincts', but simply in the forwarding agents' ignorance of animal behaviour.

Deer may themselves cause a fatal situation if their antlers become interlocked in such a way that they cannot free themselves. The rules of the game force them to go on wrestling until both die.

Another way of showing the white flag is by exposing the most vulnerable part of the body to the victor, as is done by the dog and the wolf.

Finally, a third way is to show beyond all possibility of doubt that there is not the slightest desire to fight on. The gull turns its head 180 degrees away from its opponent, or hides its beak deep in its breast plumage. The carp lays out all its fins and revolves on its longitudinal axis in such a way as to turn its back to the victor. In the Galapagos Islands the sea-lizard lies flat on its belly before the victor, stretches out its four limbs and slowly crawls away backwards. A defeated cock, if it cannot run away, hides its head in a dark hole, or in a pail or box. If in a small wire-mesh cage it can neither fly nor hide its head, the fight continues to the death. This fact is taken advantage of in the Far East to train birds for cock-fighting.

If, however, the loser is able to surrender, this immediately puts an end to its opponent's aggression. The biological significance of this bloodless duelling is that the defeated party, generally a healthy young animal, is left alive to try its luck again another day.

Killer Dove

Sometimes, especially in overbred strains of dogs, individual animals occur in whom the instinctual duelling code,

66

including the inhibition that prevents them from biting, has degenerated. Such animals are the 'habitual criminals' of the animal world. Occasionally strains of animals which lack, and are meant to lack, the inhibition against killing their kind are bred deliberately. That is the other way of producing fighting cocks.

The inhibition against biting and killing is naturally absent in animals that have no weapon capable of endangering their fellows. A few pecks with the beak hardly matter to a pigeon. The defeated bird can generally easily escape further such attentions by flying away.

But woe betide one of two rival cock-pigeons if they are shut up together in a cage without exit. The superior bird ruthlessly drives the other into a corner, and will spend hour after hour ruthlessly pecking it to death. In the unnatural conditions of incarceration the dove, the symbol of peace, becomes a merciless butcher.

5
WAR AND PEACE AMONG
THE TERMITES

Attack on the Termite Stronghold

IN the African veldt the vanguard of an army of ants reaches a termite fortress as tall as a man. Hundreds of the blood-thirsty predators swarm over the reddish-brown termite nest, while the main force, numbering tens of thousands, halts in an agitated throng immediately in front of it.

The walls of the fortress are as hard as concrete; nowhere is there the smallest hole through which they can penetrate. Nevertheless the termites within are aware of the approach of the invaders; the alarm signal has been sounded; it is a strange clicking sound, that continues for minutes on end. The termite nymphs and younger workers take refuge in the deepest parts of the structure, while older workers hastily wall up the entrances to the queen's palace and the soldiers take up their positions in the outer forts, casemates, corridor galleries and other strategic points.

Meanwhile a reconnaissance party of the invaders has found a closed chimney-like structure on the upper part of the fortress, the dark brown colour of which stands out against the lighter colour of the rest. This is a new storey added to the termites' skyscraper only a few hours ago, and here the concrete is still soft. In a flash the reconnaissance ant with its antennae 'trills' this information on to the head of its nearest fellow, and in no time the news has been 'spoken round' to the great army, which promptly swarms up the hill and begins digging into the soft mass of the newly-built structure.

Scarcely has the first breach been made than the intruders

find themselves faced with numbers of little 'gun barrels'. In this case they are up against a particularly dangerous enemy, the nasute termites (*Nasutitermes*). These do not fight with the same weapons as other termites; instead of cut-throat nippers, they have a different kind of lethal weapon. Where their head ought to be, the soldiers of these tribes have a kind of glue-tube.

Through the 'gun-barrel' of the proboscis they can spray the enemy with a foul-smelling, glutinous fluid which glues them

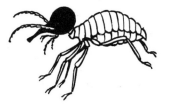

A nasute soldier of the termite state. The head of the blind animal is shaped like a tube of glue. They spray enemies through the nose with a sticky fluid and glue them to the battlefield.

to the battlefield. The range of these 'glue-guns' is of course very short. Besides, the nasute soldiers, having no eyes, have to feel with their antennae everyone they meet before knowing whether he be friend or foe.

In daylight this gives the invaders a slight advantage, as their eyes enable them to recognise an enemy (only if he moves, of course) at a distance of two centimetres, not more. So it often happens that after breaching the fortress they manage to pinch off the guards' glutinous proboscis before the glue is spurted.

The hunter, predatory or driver ants themselves increase their furious fighting spirit by means of a citral aromatic substance they secrete in special glands. They charge in a dense mass, swarming over and round each other, slaughter the guards and advance like shock troops into the labyrinth of passages and chambers inside the termite nest.

To be able to find their way out again, they leave a trail of pathfinder perfume with the point of their abdomen. Without this Ariadne's thread they would be hopelessly lost in the labyrinth, and would inevitably perish in it.

Through the breach a vast column of ants pours into the fortress. After some time the survivors of the battle reappear with their prey, dead termite soldiers, workers and nymphs, and drag them to a dumping-ground. Here the corpses are cut up in regular sizes by specialist butcher-ants and fed by 'nurses' to the ant larvae, which these creatures always take with them on their endless forays.

Only very rarely do they find the queen's palace, which lies roughly in the centre of the fortress. The passages leading to it are so confusing that the invading army is nearly always led astray.

Moreover, in the neighbourhood of their queen the defenders fight with the courage of despair. Soldier termites fight on even after all six legs have been bitten off.

Round about the queen even the workers are said to join in the battle. Observers have reported four small workers holding an absolute Goliath of an ant by the legs until a big soldier arrived and glued it down in the middle of the passage with its nose-fluid. Gradually the aggressive spirit of the invaders flags, losses increase in the face of the enemy's numerical superiority, and suddenly the whole army withdraws from the nest as if at a word of command.

Smaller nests are completely pillaged by them. In the big fortresses, however, they face millions of resolute defenders, on whom they inflict heavy losses without, however, seriously endangering their survival.

Nuptial Flight Holocaust

The vital thing is the survival of the king and queen. Even though hundreds of thousands of their 'subjects' perish in an invasion, even though on 'peaceful' days thousands of the dwellers in the stronghold are devoured by ant-eaters, ant-bears and woodpeckers, or by rapacious ground-beetle larvae, which lurk like ghosts in the wall recesses and seize termites passing in the dark, to the queen all these are trifling matters, for she lays one egg about every two seconds uninterruptedly day and night.

A queen can lay up to 48,000 eggs in a day. In the course of her ten-year life her progeny numbers hundreds of millions. If the fertility of the latter is also taken into account, a queen and her offspring could in the course of ten years populate the warmer latitudes so densely that there would be no room for a single human being or earth-worm. Fortunately the termites, whose waxy chitin integument is so filmy that the gut glistens through it, are highly-prized delicacies.

At certain seasons, shortly before dusk, when the air is sultry and thundery, the termites open their fortresses at the top. Soldiers post themselves round about in battle trim, and 'smell' whether the coast is clear or not. If there is no cause for alarm, they give a scent signal, and with explosive force hundreds of thousands of winged, sexual-form termites mount into the air like a rising column of smoke. Strange to say, they swarm out of all the neighbouring termite nests at the same time. They must have a kind of barometer in their antennae which tells them when the best conditions prevail for the nuptial flight.

The biological significance of this strange institution is that winged males and females belonging to different states meet in the air and subsequently mate. Thus the danger of inbreeding is reduced.

Moreover, an innate time-sense in conjunction with this barometer tells them to embark on the nuptial flight only when the approach of night gives them relative protection from their enemies and the ground is about to be so soaked by an approaching storm that the mating couples will quickly be able to dig themselves in.

But before that stage is reached the 'smoke-trails' of ascending swarms provoke a fierce assault by all the termite-eaters: birds, bats, hedgehogs, armadillos, ground-hogs, beetles, wasps, lizards, geckoes, chameleons, millipedes come hurrying along to secure their share of the feast.

Dr. Heinz Stephan, of the Max Planck Institute for Brain Research, describes ant-eaters, insectivores looking like fir-cones, which had so gorged themselves with termites that they were incapable of movement and he could catch hold of them. Frogs go on snapping them up in the air until the wings are hanging out of their mouths.

Also natives appear on the scene and light big camp fires. These attract the swarming insects and singe their filmy wings and grill them as they fall. If fat is available, the natives fry them in big pans. They are said to be delicious done that way.

The relatively few survivors of the holocaust, after a brief courtship, mate in the hole they have dug themselves, and produce offspring. They are now king and queen, but for lack of staff or servants during the first weeks have to do all the chores themselves – build the nest, search for food, fetch water if necessary, look after their eggs and feed the nymphs when they emerge with a milky fluid from their salivary glands. The nymphs look like tiny workers or soldiers, and are soon able to take over 'fatigue' duties. After they have made further progress, one of their first tasks is that of immuring their parents in the so-called foundation chamber, where, well protected from danger, they devote themselves entirely to the production of offspring. The only communication with the outside world is by way of small trap-doors through which nymphs, which by now have developed into fully-grown workers, are able to slip.

Secret of the Termite Architects

As the population of the new termite state increases, the crenellated fortress which is its home grows too. The termite architects and builders perform fantastic feats in this respect. A comparable human achievement would be a building as tall as the Matterhorn.

The technique employed is as follows. After a heavy shower,

A troop of ants pounce on a dead bee.

A glance at the termite state. On the left, a soldier. In the centre, eggs and a young nymph. On the right, two dark sexual-form animals and two workers. Below them, two older nymphs. The trophallaxis can be easily recognised; food is only from 1 to 5 per cent digested and is then passed on to other animals through the rectum.

The stronghold of the Australian compass termites seen from the north. Shaped like a compass needle, it is always aligned north–south to minimise solar radiation during the noonday heat. How the creatures determine the points of the compass is still unknown.

workers open the top of the fortress from within. Soldiers then emerge and take up position in a circle of some twelve inches in diameter round the hole.

Then workers appear, each dragging a small clump of earth, which (in the case of *Macrotermes natalensis*) he has fetched, not from the surface humus, which is unsuitable for building purposes, but from much deeper strata and is so constituted that much harder concrete can be made of it. Each worker with his load makes his way in between two soldiers and begins mixing cement. His method is to squeeze out of his mouth a brownish sausage of half-digested wood and saliva, and he works this up with the clump of earth into a uniform mass. Single pillars begin to rise between the soldiers, and when they are finished they are joined by round arches. The walls are then completed and the structure closed in the shape of a dome. Thus these sightless creatures complete the extension to their home with a sleepwalker's assurance and after only a few hours' work.

The whole phenomenon surpasses our comprehension. How do these small, blind creatures, working without a plan, visualise the grand design they follow in building these great structures? The following experiment illustrates the nature of this baffling question.

Before the soldiers had, so to speak, drawn up the ground-plan by forming up in a circle, the 'building site' was divided in two by a thick steel-plate wall, making it impossible for the termites on one side to communicate by sight, sound, smell or touch with their fellows on the other. By human standards this should have led the little creatures astray. It seemed reasonable to assume at least that the building would be un-symmetrical, or that the dome arches would fail to meet. But the ants simply treated the steel plate as non-existent and incorporated it into the structure.

This makes the phenomenon more baffling still, and we are still without the slightest clue to a plausible scientific explanation.

Termites are capable of still more extraordinary feats, in comparison with which those just described are quite elementary. They can, for instance, instal an air-conditioning system in their fortress, by which they are able to regulate the temperature, humidity and the oxygen – and carbon dioxide – content of the air. This marvel was investigated by Professor Martin Lüscher, of Berne University, in the nests of *Macrotermes natalensis* on the Ivory Coast, which are up to sixteen feet in height.

These termites require a tropical hothouse temperature of 86 degrees Fahrenheit (30 degrees Centigrade), with 98 to 99 per cent air humidity. If the humidity drops only a little, they die within from five to ten hours. So they have to stock themselves up with humidity in their home before they set out on their marches of several hundred yards through subterranean passages to such sources of food supply as rotting trees, houses, telegraph poles, railway sleepers, sugar-cane plantations and titbits of wood, wool, leather or ivory.

The water required to maintain their extraordinarily high humidity rate is brought up by specialist water-bearer termites through long tunnels which descend to the ground-water level, which in dry areas is sometimes 150 feet below the surface. To maintain an even temperature, the two million inhabitants of an average-sized termite state do not rely on the natural heat of the tropics, which is subject to violent fluctuations. Instead, they generate heat themselves by means of their own metabolism and the metabolism of the many fungus-gardens they carefully cultivate inside their home.

To keep their private climate as constant as possible and independent of outside fluctuations, they effectively insulate themselves within outer walls which are half a yard thick and as hard as concrete. But they also have to breathe. Two million termites consume 26,500 pints of fresh air and exhale about 530 pints of carbon dioxide in a day. How do these waste gases escape, and how is the oxygen essential to life brought in?

The answer is a highly efficient ventilation system. Round the outside of the termitary there are a dozen ascending ridges. These are the 'cooling-fins' of the installation, which the termites 'invented' millions of years before man. In each of these ridges, about ten narrow air-shafts lead from top to bottom just under the surface. The hot, used air collects in the 'attic', passes down through the air-shafts, where it cools, and

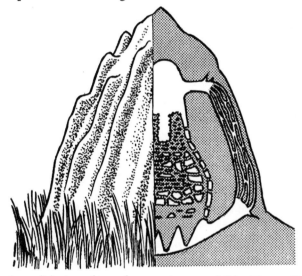

The air-conditioning plant of a termite stronghold. The cooling-fins visible externally contain ventilation shafts through which air passes down into the underground vault. From here the whole nest is aired.

at the same time unites with the outside air through microscopically minute pores in the walls, sheds carbon dioxide and absorbs fresh oxygen.

From these 'lungs' the revitalised air at the correct temperature passes into the spacious vaulted chambers which lie at a depth of about three feet underground. Here, on a number of supporting pillars constructed on mechanically sound principles, lies the real termites' nest, continuously supplied with fresh air from the vaults below.

In the hundred or so air-shafts inside the cooling-fins termite 'mechanics' are continually at work contracting or widening air outlets on a valve principle, closing or opening shafts according to the time of day or season, depending on whether the temperature is too cold or too hot or whether there is too much or too little oxygen.

The astonishing feature is that the ventilation is so regulated that the optimum temperature always prevails at the centre of the nest, and thus in the queen's palace, though the mechanics are at a distance of three or four yards in a bee-line from the queen.

Who or what keeps the mechanics continually informed about the atmospheric situation in the queen's palace, so that they know whether to throttle back or 'turn up' the ventilation? Do messengers come running to them? In view of the distances in the labyrinth, they would spend some hours on the way. Do the mechanics have an appropriate 'theoretical value control'?

In view of the different nest sizes and the constantly changing conditions inside and outside, this would be subject to such complicated fluctuations that such a hypothesis seems untenable.

Does the queen send signals with special aromatic substances reporting changes of temperature? That would be a phenomenon unique in nature.

Their ventilation technique is sufficiently sophisticated to be adaptable to climatic conditions in any part of Africa, and also enables them to survive in Central European conditions. They are not found in Europe for the sole reason that new colonies of *Macrotermes natalensis* can be founded only by swarming sexual-form animals, and in the initial phase, when they are entirely dependent on themselves, they are not capable of surviving in the temperate zone, as their foundation chamber lacks the air-conditioning plant.

If *Macrotermes natalensis* were able, like other species of termites, to found new colonies by digging underground galleries, all wooden buildings and objects in Europe would be threatened, if not destroyed by them.

Welfare State

No less astonishing than termite architecture is their state organisation. As we mentioned above, the queen lays an egg about every two seconds. Consequently she gradually swells into a huge, shapeless paunch about four inches long, an immobile egg-laying machine, while the king retains his diminutive size, crawls busily about her and fertilises her from time to time.

After each substantial extension of the fortress, the workers offer the royal couple a new, bigger and still better protected palace. In a fantastic procession, during which whole inside walls are pulled down and special ramps and roads built and tunnels widened, with infinite toil and trouble the immobile queen is dragged millimetre by millimetre by about a hundred workers to the new home in which she and her husband are again promptly immured.

Through the few hatches that are left open workers make their way unflaggingly in an almost endless stream to stuff a special food, in the form of a salivary secretion, into the queen's mouth, and at her hinder end they no less incessantly carry away the freshly laid eggs. The wood-pulp food brought in by the harvest workers changes hands up to ten times and passes through ten stomachs and several guts before it is fully digested. The distribution of this communal food is carried out on an astonishing equal-shares-for-all basis. The hungrier a termite is, the more rarely does it offer its fellows food from the 'social stomach' and the more frequently does it beg from passers-by. If a very hungry, begging termite meets a companion who begs even more importunately than itself, it unhesitatingly gives of the little it has in its stomach.

Thus the nutritional condition of the whole state always remains approximately constant. None go hungry while others are well fed, there are no poor and rich. With ingenious simplicity they have developed a practically complete welfare state. Similar conditions prevail among bees and ants.

In addition to the ordinary food, the queen exudes through her skin a thickish fluid which is particularly attractive to the workers. It is quickly passed on by the palace staff to other members of the state. There is something mysterious about this fluid. The biochemists have not established its composition and effects. It may be connected with the strange phenomenon by which such entirely different creatures as blind soldiers, blind workers and both sighted and winged sexual animals are born from one and the same kind of egg.

One species of termite found in the Mediterranean area develops as many as fifty-six different types of specialist – harvest workers, water-bearers, builders, fungus gardeners, nurses for the young, alarm-sounders, soldiers, police and many others.

One task which falls to the police is that of killing off the sick, the crippled, the disabled and the idle. A kind of cannibalism is practised with these. The bodies are dumped in a kind of mortuary, where they presumably serve as an emergency food reserve.

The soldiers, as observation has repeatedly shown, are specially trained for war service. Dummy battles take place between pairs of contestants, who practise hemming each other in and forcing each other down; they try out lethal 'holds' and engage in all sorts of trials of strength, which always end without bloodshed or injury.

All that is yet known is that the production of these very different kinds of creatures is governed by two pairs of glands. One pair secretes a skin-shedding hormone which promotes the formation of certain parts of the body such as eyes and wings. The other produces a youth hormone, which checks the processes of development, maturing and ageing. If the skin-shedding hormone gland increases in size, the normal evolution into a sexual animal ensues, that is, into a youthful image of one royal parent. If, however, this gland remains small, the individual becomes a nymph of inhibited development, a eunuch, a worker. But if at a certain stage in the nymph both pairs of glands are suddenly enlarged fivefold, giant larvae with powerful heads, future soldiers, come into being.

If the termite queen suddenly dies, all the other members of that particular state do not, as was assumed in the first period of research on termites, mysteriously perish at the same time. In reality far more fantastic things occur. Out of the broad mass of simple, sexless workers some animals are selected and fed in such a way that their youth hormone gland is enormously enlarged. By this means workers are transformed into queens.

The growth of the glands can be determined by the termites themselves by means of appropriate nutrition. A decisive part in this is played by the amount of Vitamin T (which was discovered only a few years ago) that is fed to the rising generation, and its timing. This vitamin is the most important product of the termite fungi, which are cultivated in numerous chambers of the nest and tended by workers specially 'trained' for the task.

6

PRAIRIE-DOG TOWN

Moon-landscape on Earth

MODERN astronomy has robbed us of the illusion of an inhabited moon landscape. But in the wide prairies of North America, in the former Wild West, there are regions in which the surface of the earth looks like a moon landscape in miniature.

There thousands of little craters, each about eighteen inches high and six feet in diameter, rise from the prairie grass. Over an area of some 100 acres there are craters about every ten yards. If a human being walks through this world of craters, like Gulliver in Lilliput, a marmot-like creature barks fiercely at him from practically every crater. If he trespasses on a crater, the barker vanishes into the hole with a nasal 'yip', only to begin scolding still more furiously a few seconds later from another crater. We are at an entrance to a labyrinthine subterranean city inhabited by about a thousand prairie-dogs.

The name 'prairie-dog' was given to these animals about a century ago, when they barked in their thousands at the early white settlers. But their bark is really the only thing these creatures have in common with dogs. They are near relations of the marmots, and are of the same stock as the squirrel family, though they weigh more than two pounds and are thus much more solid than our droll tree acrobats.

In the Black Hills country of South Dakota the young American zoologist Dr. John A. King, now of the Roscoe B. Jackson Memorial Laboratory, Bar Harbor, Maine, accompanied by his wife, camped for three summers and one winter very close to these little moon-crater dwellers and observed their curious community life with the aid of field-glasses and telephoto lenses. When he lived like an Indian in the open prairie, he had not yet been awarded his doctor's degree, which he gained with a thesis which reads like a chapter out of *Gulliver's Travels*.

In fact he carried out a piece of valuable pioneering in an important field of animal behaviour, for the study of animals living in communities is still in its early stages. The factors that cause animals to live in communities are of great interest to the biologist. An animal must have a hereditary disposition to make it capable of community life. Often it has no ties with its closest relatives. Eggs are laid or young born without the parents troubling about them any further. Even mating is often merely a transient encounter. Certainly there are 'friendships' and marriages among animals that last for years. But in the flock, the swarm and the herd ties are as a rule impersonal and anonymous. These were therefore called 'anonymous' units by the late Dr. Kramer, the German biologist, who was head of a department at Wilhelmshaven of the Max Planck Institute for Physiology of Behaviour.

The problem of how this community living came to be established in the course of thousands or hundreds of thousands of years and came to assume fixed ritual forms could be studied in especially favourable conditions in the case of prairie-dogs, because their 'state unit', unlike packs of wolves, swarms of migratory birds or 'schools' of fish, is not perpetually on the move, but is confined to a fixed territory, which is abandoned only in times of disaster.

At first sight the crater landscape seems to be inhabited by a totally unorganised throng, but on closer observation a firmly established social order appears out of the apparent chaos. Like a human town, the prairie-dog town is divided into districts — there are about two dozen of them, each inhabited by a clan of about forty members.

Unlike districts in a town, however, they are separated from each other by 'walls' — invisible walls consisting of scent trails marking the boundaries. But there is a taboo on crossing them, and they are not crossed except with warlike intent.

'Moon-crater' city of the prairie-dogs.

Earthly Paradise for the Young

Each district is about thirty yards long and thirty yards wide, and is generally occupied by three or four families, which are not inter-related. The ruling buck, a senior who has proved himself in battle, is of a different family, and the district is his by right of conquest. He is the lord and master of three, four, five or six females long domiciled there and a swarm of twenty or thirty young, born during this or the previous year. Occasionally a district is inhabited solely by an elderly childless couple, who live there in untroubled peace and harmony.

For the prairie-dog young, conditions are those of an earthly paradise, as they have reason to discover at the age of two or three weeks, when they first venture out of their cave nest, crawl through the labyrinth of dark, subterranean passages and chambers alone, and finally, dazzled by the first sight of sunlight, curiously thrust their heads over the wall of a crater.

Two or three adults promptly appear, and kiss, sniff at and caress the newcomer. A host of young prairie-dogs come skipping along from neighbouring craters, and in a moment the first games are under way; the young animals chase each other through the prairie grass, dash round the tall thistles or play 'I'm the king of the castle'.

When the young prairie-dog feels hungry, it does not waste time looking for its mother. It nestles up against the first fully-grown animal it comes across, and tries to suck. Generally, of course, it will turn out to be somebody else's mother, but no matter. To the young prairie-dog this moon-crater landscape is a land flowing with milk and honey, for no female will refuse it the breast, and it is always able to assuage its prodigious appetite.

Its youth and ignorance, however, may cause it to seek nourishment from a male. In that event the latter, so far from showing annoyance and pushing it away, seems to appreciate that the mistake is based purely on inexperience. It hugs the baby, rolls it over on its back and play all sorts of paternal pranks with it till the two are squeaking delightedly.

Like a spoilt child, the young prairie-dog grows cheekier day by day. It particularly enjoys holding on to the tail of a grown-up animal and being dragged along.

If a grown-up ignores it in spite of repeated appeals to it to play, it jumps on its back and keeps skipping about until the elder gives in and joins in a romp.

In the evening it does not dream of returning to its mother's nest. It curls up in a strange 'bed' wherever it happens to have been playing, and is hospitably received wherever it goes. Its mother is just as hospitable to little strangers.

This community care for the rising generation is the reason

83

why the mortality among young prairie-dogs is so extra-ordinarily low. In one whole summer John A. King recorded only one death among fifty-eight new-born animals.

'Air-raid' Alarm

One day, while the usual wild games were in progress, there was a sudden series of quick, shrill whistles, which sounded as alarming as the wail of a siren. All the prairie-dogs throughout the town who had been unconcernedly eating grass or playing disappeared in a flash.

What had happened? John A. King and his wife scoured the area with field-glasses, but at first could see nothing. Then, high in the sky, looking as small as a comma at half a yard's distance, they made out a slowly circling bird of prey.

Thanks to their highly efficient observer corps system, all the prairie-dogs were safely in their air-raid shelters before the hawk had time to begin its nose-dive. Observation posts are continually manned on the highest craters all over the town, and on the slightest suspicion the whole population is driven underground by an agitated whistle. As soon as it sounds, every animal dashes headlong down the nearest crater-hole, not waiting to see what sort of danger threatens.

In the event of a ground-level emergency, the animals be-have differently. A short nasal 'yip' proclaims the fact that a coyote, badger or ferret is slinking about, but this is not re-garded as especially disturbing. For one thing, only the resi-dents in the outskirts and suburbs are endangered, and for another, prairie-dogs have a whole range of stratagems with which to dupe their ground-level enemies.

When the alert is sounded, all who have heard it climb to a crater rampart and keep a look-out for the raider. If it turns out that the latter's objective is neighbours of no account about a hundred yards away, they resume eating and playing as un-concernedly as ever.

Dwellers in the most dangerous areas, the outskirts, take effective measures to protect themselves against surprise attack. A raider's only chance of catching a prairie-dog is to steal up under cover of bushes and large shrubs unobserved by the sentries and to pounce on it unawares. All plants that might provide such cover are therefore removed by the little rodents, who clear a thirty- to forty-yard-wide observation belt, like a fire-zone, round their home.

Moreover, these astonishing operations at the approaches to the city are only part of their agricultural skills. Between the crater forts inside the city they systematically cultivate nutrient plants, including certain feed grasses and juicy thistles that supply their water requirements.

Their method of cultivation is as simple as it is effective. It resembles that used by man 10,000 years ago, when he was developing from a hunting and food-gathering nomad into a sedentary tiller of the soil. All inedible plants are torn out by the roots, dried in the sun and then taken to a rubbish-dump or scattered in the prairie far outside the observation zones. In this way only plants of nutritive value to the animals multiply in the town area.

But to go back to the 'invasion alarm'. Badgers can be more dangerous than coyotes, for they follow fleeing prairie dogs into their homes. As they are more bulky, however, they have to stop and dig every now and then in the subterranean passages. They certainly work very quickly with their sharp claws, but they never manage to catch an experienced prairie-dog. It has not yet been established whether or not beasts of prey remain permanently as uninvited guests in the crater town, which they would indeed regard as an inexhaustible meat store.

The all-clear signal is a regular shout of joy. Every single prairie-dog rises on its hind legs, holds out its forepaws like someone walking in his sleep, throws back its head and utters a series of dissyllabic sounds with such force that the vibration sends it hopping off the ground.

The other animals immediately emerge from their subterranean labyrinth, stand on the rims of the craters and join in the shrill cries, as if at a victory celebration. Even the youngest do their best to join in. But almost invariably they lose their balance in the excitement and tumble over backwards at the first sound they make.

This shout of joy, however, has yet another meaning in prairie-dog language, as the young find out for themselves in a thoroughly unpleasant way as soon as they have mastered it.

As they grow older, they grow more adventurous and venture farther and farther afield, and end by inadvertently overstepping the boundary, the scent 'wall' that divides their district from its neighbours. These boundaries are always closely guarded; the bucks in control of the area patrol them early and late. They continually climb a crater, and keep a watchful eye on their neighbours across the border. They cover a distance of about a mile and a half daily in the course of these police duties.

Whenever they catch sight of another prairie-dog in their territory, they hurry to investigate. Prairie-dogs, capable of identifying a bird of prey when it is an almost invisible speck in the sky, are strangely 'short-sighted' in relation to each other. The animal on police duty goes to within kissing range of the other, opens its mouth slightly and bares its teeth, ready to snap if it should turn out to be an intruder.

If it is a member of the same clan, it ducks and wags its tail joyfully, and the policeman's menacing gesture changes into a protracted, kiss-like nuzzling of two snouts. A buck will roll a female on her back, still maintaining the 'kiss-contact'. They will fondle each other for a while, stretch out at full length side by side and then get up and go on eating, their bodies still pressed close together, until the buck continues his roving alone.

A curious thing is that this 'kiss of friendship' is such a ritual that it is even actually exchanged during flight from enemies, though very quickly and cursorily.

Intruders in a strange district do not take the risk of coming within kissing range of the seasoned fighter in possession, but make off in good time. They take the shortest route to the boundary, for if they are caught there will be bites and bloodshed. A prairie-dog running fast is an object of suspicion, and is promptly pursued by all the residents of the district. There can be only two reasons for such haste. Either the animal is an intruder with a guilty conscience, who must be driven off, or a kinsman in trouble, who needs help.

A slight error about the exact course of a boundary can lead to a squabble between two neighbours. John A. King tells this story about one of these comical incidents.

One day a female feeding on grass was evidently not quite clear about the exact course of the boundary, which she overstepped by barely half a yard. A female from the territory thus unlawfully violated approached cautiously, fiercely showing her teeth, until the two noses were nearly in contact, and stared at the intruder in perplexity. The stranger evidently believed herself to be in the right, for she refused to be diverted. She placidly turned about, raised and spread out her tail, exposing her buttocks with the anal glands, and allowed the other female to sniff.

This, as among dogs, is a way of declaring one's identity. It is equivalent to saying something like: 'This is my scent mark. It smells exactly the same as our boundary, though there is no sign of that here. So be off with you and leave me alone.' The other female then showed her buttocks. This alternating display was repeated several times, until one of the two lost patience and abruptly bit the other in the buttocks.

The bitten female ran away in fright, but stopped after a few yards, turned and began the squabble all over again. The two animals kept running backwards and forwards, giving each other several harmless bites and displaying their scent mark every now and then. In the end both of them picked up the scent of the boundary line, which had obviously grown very faint, and went their separate ways, taking no further notice of each other.

Thus the district boundaries are carefully guarded and preserved for generation after generation without change. In his three years of observation of a town inhabited by more than a thousand prairie-dogs, John A. King failed to detect a single real violation of boundaries. The explanation lies in the little scent-display squabbles which lead to the immediate rectification of a disputed boundary. It would be interesting to find out whether the boundaries remain unchanged for decades or perhaps still longer periods.

Conquerors and Pioneers

Strangely enough, if an ignorant young prairie-dog skips across the closely guarded boundary, it is left alone. The love of the young shown by grown animals even extends to those from 'foreign parts', though to the latter neither milk nor shelter is offered – a tactful way of persuading them to leave.

If, however, the young intruder dares stand on a crater hill and give vent to his cheerful feelings with a joyful cry, this blissful state of affairs ends immediately. For in prairie-dog language the cry of joy, in addition to denoting well-being and the all-clear after an attack by beasts of prey, has yet another meaning. This is: 'Here I stand. Around me is my kingdom.' Such a statement by a young intruder is felt to be the height of presumption, and so the disconcerted youngster is at once angrily expelled. In the weeks that follow the exact course of the boundary is made plain to him in unmistakable fashion.

Even in its own district, however, the golden age of youth comes to its inevitable end. This occurs at the age of one, when spring comes, and it discovers the attractions of the female sex. Henceforward its father keeps a stern eye on it. The time comes when it must shake off family ties and leave its childhood home.

Two alternatives are open to it. Either it can try to conquer a new quarter for itself by driving out the male in possession, or it can migrate to an uninhabited area and, in conjunction with other congenial pioneering spirits, clear the land, build

The powerful head of a termite of the soldier caste with pincer-shaped lower jaws shaped into tongs. The creature is blind. It has two 'pearl-necklace' feelers instead of eyes.

Affectionate exchange of kisses between a young and an adult prairie-dog. After this they romp and roll around together and end by uttering squeals of joy.

Alerted by a sentry's whistle, the prairie-dogs are on the watch for a ground enemy.

subterranean passages, chambers and craters, and thus enlarge the prairie-dog town.

At night the pioneers go on sleeping in their old homes. At first their bond with home is not severed, but only relaxed. Very early in the morning, while their neighbours are still asleep, they scamper undisturbed through alien districts to the new territory. The work there is very arduous. The soil dug out to form the crater has to be piled up and shaped. When heavy rain has softened it, it has to be flattened and made firm with the nose, inch by inch, and the work goes on relentlessly, hour after hour and day after day. This pioneering work is also very dangerous. Before the labyrinths, observation craters and visibility zones are finished, no fewer than half the colonists die or are eaten by birds or beasts of prey.

In the evening the survivors go home to sleep, again scampering at full tilt through hostile districts. This pattern is repeated every day until the middle of June, when the new home wrested from the inhospitable prairie is finished and can be finally occupied.

Very different is the behaviour of the young males who feel strong enough to conquer an existing district for themselves. They begin by undertaking reconnaissance patrols into neighbouring districts, to find out which male in possession is oldest or weakest and where their chances are best.

When a young animal has decided that his chances are favourable in a particular district, the most difficult part of his campaign begins. It is not sufficient merely to drive out the old ruler of the roost by sheer muscular strength and biting prowess. That gets him practically nowhere, for the population of the district may maintain their allegiance to their defeated ruler and abandon his territory with him, leaving his successor mateless, without subjects and alone.

So weeks before the decisive struggle the pretender has to undertake propaganda for himself in hostile territory. This makes high demands on his tact, diplomacy and impudence, for all the animals of the district to be won tend by nature to sound the alarm on the appearance of an intruder in their midst and to chase him away in a kind of battle, biting him fiercely.

But here too the secret of success is persistence. The aspirant's policy must be to remain in the hostile territory at all costs. When he is chased he must simply describe a semicircle without leaving the territory. If the pressure becomes too great and he is really forced out, after a few minutes' rest in his own territory he must cross the border again at another point. An important thing to remember is the need to behave as unobtrusively as possible. Someone sniffing around someone else's craters is acting as if they were already his own. Attempts to exchange loving little kisses with the females, behaving very affectionately towards them, may eventually lead to success.

For the time being a serious showdown with the male in possession is scrupulously avoided. The aspirant merely allows himself to be chased by him, as a kind of trial of strength. His objective is above all to allow him no peace from morning till night. In this way the younger animal gauges the strong and weak points of the older, and thus prepares himself for the decisive struggle.

Sometimes he realises he has no chance. In that case he gives up without a battle, reconnoitres another district or goes to the outskirts and becomes a pioneer.

7

GUESTS IN THE BABOON STATE

Military Protection on the March

PROFESSOR S. L. WASHBURN and Dr. Irven DeVore, who were at the time Professor and Assistant Professor of Anthropology at the University of California at Berkeley, succeeded, with the aid of a stratagem to which we shall return later, in gaining admission, practically as 'full members in good standing', to a band of eighty baboons. For months they ranged the plains of East Africa with these creatures, and thus discovered some remarkable details about their private life, social organisation and military operations. The record of their experiences forms one of the most exciting chapters in the history of modern animal behaviour research.

A new day is dawning on the plain of Amboseli. Against the bluish-black infinity the majestic ice dome of Kilimanjaro sparkles in the first gleam of morning amid the fading stars.

A chorus of grunts and screams begins in a clump of six thorn trees. They seem to be covered all over with giant fruits, but when it grows light it turns out that a band of eighty baboons is just waking up.

At night, when the carnivores and snakes of the African plains are at their liveliest, the baboons sleep as high up as possible in tall trees, sitting close together on their hard-skinned buttocks.

At least one-third of the animals keep watch at all times, so as to be able to give the alarm at the approach of danger. There is no need of any formal 'changing of the guard'; during the hours of darkness all baboons suffer from a deep-rooted, primitive anxiety which continually startles them into wakefulness and allows them to fall asleep again only when utterly exhausted.

This deep-rooted primitive fear of the thousand invisible dangers of the African night is the reason why they are in no hurry to get up in the morning. The whole company look decidedly sleepy and cross, and they do not descend from their perch in the trees until it is broad daylight. But then they at once draw up in a formation comparable to that of troops advancing into hostile territory, with strict march discipline and continual preparedness for all-round defence. First to move forward into the open plain is the advance guard, consisting of four or five males of average strength and one or two young males whose strength is already pretty well developed. The main force follows well within range of vision; first the childless females and young males, then a ring of seasoned warriors surrounding the females and the young. Last comes the rearguard, which is a replica of the advance guard. Every time a tree is passed a scout climbs it and keeps a look-out.

Before the column has gone very far two wild dogs, barking loudly, come dashing towards it from the left. The throng of women and children promptly scatter towards the nearest clump of trees, but the troop of warriors seem straightaway to realise the triviality of the danger. They merely draw a little closer together and trot on steadily, as if the dogs were unworthy of further notice.

When the dogs make as if to approach the mother animals and their children, there is a whistle. Like lightning the baboons form up into a barrier between the dogs and their fleeing relatives, growling viciously and with bared teeth. The dogs stop dead, as if rooted to the spot, and when the most powerful baboon breaks rank and makes a furious dummy attack on them they run off helter-skelter.

After this excitement there is a big palaver. The animals have grown rather uncertain about which direction to take. A curious thing about baboon communities is that, unlike many other animals, their destination is not laid down dictatorially by a leader. Instead, a kind of custom or tradition seems to prevail which broadly governs their travels through their territory, though there are frequent changes of plan depending on unexpected circumstances, the weather and the mood of the moment – all of them matters which are thoroughly discussed in big pow-wows.

Repulse of the Leopards

While the situation is still being reviewed in this way, a scout on one of the neighbouring trees appears to have seen something. He hurries down, gesticulating wildly, grunting, smacking his lips and making faces. The other animals obviously understand his meaning. They promptly resume formation and set off again at a lively pace.

The objective is a herd of thirty Impala antelopes, to whom the arrival of the baboons appears to be very welcome, for as soon as they scent them they hurry forward to meet them. What sort of curious friendship can this be between animals so different as the baboon and the impala, or black-heeled antelope?

Strange as it may seem, the partnership between the two species on the grassy plains provides security for both. From the tree-tops baboons, with their excellent eyesight, can spot an enemy at a great distance, while those hidden by the tall grass or thick brushwood are detected by the impalas, whose sense of smell is exceptionally acute. Moreover, baboons and impalas understand each other's alarm calls and other signals, and know what sort of enemy the other has detected and what counter-measures must be taken accordingly.

This friendship is soon to be put to the test. Not long after the meeting a baboon scout in a tree spies three leopards stealing up against the wind, a fact which he reports by means of a deep, soft 'O-O-O'. The impalas would normally dash away as soon as they scented their mortal foes. Now, however, they go on grazing unconcernedly, apparently ignoring the baboon's leopard-alarm signal.

They do not even look up to watch the baboon guard draw

93

up in close-formation battle order and advance intrepidly in the direction of the leopards, while the females and the young take refuge in the tree-tops. Only when the veteran baboon chieftain, baring his teeth, breaks rank and advances on the leopards with a loud cry of rage and drives them off into the open plain do they spare him a momentary glance of satisfaction.

Friendship Ceremony

A baboon community, like a human one, splits up into various cliques and groups. These stick faithfully together year after year. They march, eat, sleep, play with and delouse each other to their heart's content. The interesting thing is that these groups are not held together by bonds of kinship, but simply and solely by personal sympathy and friendship.

Baboon friendships are formed in a highly ceremonial manner. The one who makes the advances, generally a young animal, approaches a baboon whom he finds especially congenial, stands about two yards away from him, turns towards him his bare buttocks, which change to a deeper red, looks over his shoulder at him and utters an appealing 'la-la-la' cry. The act of turning the reddening buttocks towards an individual is a token of respect, submission and peaceable intentions.

The recipient of these attentions may decline the offer of friendship by turning away or simply ignoring the approach. But if he accepts it, he indicates the fact by momentarily mounting the buttocks so invitingly presented. This action symbolises taking possession of the new friend and the latter's duty of obedience in the future. In the ape community new members must 'work' their way up from the lowest rung.

In most clans the leader is a well-tried, powerful male. The more muscular he is, the greater the spell in which he holds the young males and the admiring females. He never has to use physical force to maintain his supremacy and hold his group together. With many animals things are different.

The impala male, for instance, spends half his life preventing his 'subjects' from running away, filching the young from other impala groups and repelling efforts to entice them from his own. All that the baboon has to do, however, is graciously to permit his subjects to scratch him.

Moreover, in the baboon community there is a rigid social hierarchy in which every animal from the strongest adult male to the smallest child has his fixed place, with corresponding rights and duties. The animals of higher status claim the best places for fodder, rest and sleep, and their juniors have to give way to them.

Professor Washburn was able quite quickly to grade all the baboons in the troop. Whenever he threw a piece of food between two animals, the one of higher rank composedly took it for himself, while the inferior hardly dared even to peep at it; he was allowed only a sideways squint from the corner of his eye. If an inferior ventures to do more than that, he is called to order, with a degree of sternness depending on the extent of his impertinence. A threatening growl is generally enough. If it is not, the senior in rank assumes the posturing attitude on all fours, ruffles up his hair, beats the ground with his right hand and goes through the motions of wiping the floor with the disrespectful creature – a method of punishment that is in fact sometimes used on the young. If the senior can find a stone, he bangs the ground with it. But a baboon never uses a stone for striking or throwing at another baboon or beast of prey. Even in a fit of ungovernable rage he will only fling it wildly away.

This threatening behaviour can be regarded as a step in evolution towards the use of weapons. Chimpanzees are in this respect a step further ahead. As Professor Adriaan Kortlandt, of Amsterdam, found on an expedition to the Congo in 1960, wild chimpanzees are extraordinarily pugnacious, and on the slightest provocation will pick up the biggest stick available to belabour their enemies with, including leopards.

95

If junior male baboons, disobedient females or impertinent young animals continue their refractory behaviour in spite of this impressive threat, the senior calls them to order with a bite in the neck. If this too fails, a dangerous biting match begins, in which the junior tries to establish precedence over his former senior. However, the precedence of a male baboon does not depend merely on strength, fighting spirit or ability to impress; it depends primarily on his 'connexions', that is to say, on the group to which he belongs. As his group supports him unreservedly in all disputes with other members of the band, all the baboons of the strongest group, together with its females and young, are at the top of the social scale, even if individual animals of other groups are more powerful physically. A cry from one of the brawlers, that is to say, the one that is losing, summons up reinforcements from his group who will help to extricate him from his predicament. The mere appearance of reinforcements is generally sufficient to restore peace.

Rarely, however, the other baboon may also call for help, and then his group also joins in. In that case the result is a general scuffle, with the fortune of war constantly changing.

Such incidents can be described as revolts in the baboon state, as they may result in a privileged group being displaced by another. Once the order of precedence has been made abundantly clear, however, major or minor squabbles are exceedingly rare, and the males no longer come to blows, even about a female.

Odd Sex Life

The sex life of baboons is very peculiar. A male, whatever his rank, does not monopolise any female for longer than a few hours or days at most. No male, not even the 'chieftain', has more than one 'wife' at a time. In the baboon state groups form to which females are admitted, but there are no harems.

If a female desires to mate, she leaves her circle of friends and her growing child and struts across to a group of males. At first she is unpretentious and ogles only the weaker males or the older youngsters. She expresses her intentions by displaying her reddening buttocks, at the same time smacking her lips and flashing her eyes.

If the male of her choice shows no interest, she gently scratches his coat and tries again. If she meets with another rebuff, she transfers her attentions to another male. But she is not content to be put off with a weaker one; on the contrary, her pretensions in regard to male strength and status increase with every rebuff. If at last, after many attempts, she comes to terms with a male, something very unexpected occurs. The bridegroom seals the association by giving her the punitive bite in the neck we have mentioned, not of course roughly or so as to cause pain, but with great tenderness, indeed, almost as a symbolic act. After that the two bashfully disappear from the scene for a few hours.

The greatest sensation in baboon life is the birth of a child. News of the happy event spreads like lightning, and everyone comes crowding round to admire the infant. Those who can get close enough gently scratch and caress the mother and go through the motions of grooming the baby too. But they only go through the motions, for the baby may be touched only by its mother. Almost Madonna-like scenes may take place on these occasions, as animal experts have repeatedly confirmed.

From its birth to the end of its life of thirty to forty years the baboon spends several hours every day in scratching and being deloused. Every baboon has its daily task of personal hygiene. Adult females are possessed by an absolutely fanatical delousing mania. They groom children, youngsters, female friends and every male who comes their way. Grooming is generally done on a reciprocal basis. He who has scratched scratches his scratcher, who lies at ease with limbs outstretched, shuts his eyes and shows every sign of bliss.

A newborn baboon must from birth be able to cling fast to its mother's breast hair, in readiness for travel at a moment's notice. The mother helps to some extent, and puts the babe to her breast with one hand. But as soon as the troop moves on it must be able to hang on by itself. The clinging reflex is fully developed in the first hours of life.

Later, at about the age of four weeks, the young ape learns to swing itself on to its mother's back, where it clings flat on its belly, until one day it boldly sits up astride.

Soon it grows more daring, and tries its first steps on the ground. At first the anxious mother holds it by the tail and takes it wherever she goes, like a dog on a lead. When it has acquired sufficient skill not to tumble down immediately from every rock and every tree, it begins abandoning its mother's side for longer and longer periods and plays with the older children.

Keeping Order in the Nursery

High jinks prevail in the baboon nursery. The children take big sticks and bang them on stones and tree-trunks, the noisier the better, and fling them wildly away and dash after them. A great favourite is the game of 'mothers and children'. Though they have not yet outgrown their mother's care, they put stones on each another's behinds and try with tail raised to carry them exactly as mothers carry their young sitting astride them. They chase each other through the tree-tops, pull each other's tails and generally have a high old time. Sometimes a 'teenager' treats a youngster roughly, in which case the latter only needs to scream, whereupon grown-ups promptly come to his assistance. Should a troop of incorrigible young toughs interfere in the play, a fully-grown male assumes supervision of the nursery, and does not hesitate to box the ears of, or 'wipe the floor' with, the worst teenagers.

In the midst of all this activity, the munching of grass, fruits, buds and young shoots and the cracking of nuts, the play and the delousing, the troop suddenly makes preparations for departure. Before the heat of the day reaches its maximum it is considered necessary to visit a neighbouring water-hole, known to the baboons from long experience.

This is one of the most dangerous undertakings of the day, for lions, the only animals, apart from snakes, that are dangerous to a compact troop of baboons, may be lying in wait there. Accordingly the troop advances slowly and cautiously. In any case it covers only from two to five miles a day.

Even so, there is a sick baboon who cannot keep up. All day he has dragged himself wearily along with the rest, but now his strength fails him, and he is left to his fate. This is a strange phenomenon. Even in remote ages men cared for the sick and injured; and other animals, elephants for instance, stay with the sick until they recover or collapse and die. When a porpoise or dolphin is knocked unconscious on a reef, his companions hold him with his blow-hole above water to enable him to breathe until he comes round. Male sperm whales stay beside their harpooned wives until they die themselves, or carry wounded young ones in their huge mouth above water level for days on end. But, in spite of the high level of their community life, there seems to be no trace of helpfulness to the sick and injured among baboons.

Every baboon separated from his troop is as good as lost. He can look forward to a gruesome death from hyenas or jackals, which show great respect for the teeth of a compact troop of baboons. Only baboon mothers have occasionally been reported as dragging their dead child round with them for weeks. During this time they are said to be quite dazed and distracted, and hardly eat. Their behaviour expresses something like genuine mourning.

At the water-hole the apes' worst fears seem to be confirmed. The vanguard stops at the last trees that offer a refuge. From here a distance of forty yards through high grass has to be negotiated to reach the water. But no other animal is in sight. If giraffes or zebras were quenching their thirst, the baboons could approach without anxiety. But what does this solitude mean? Have lions just seized an antelope, and are they now enjoying a gory meal? In that case the baboons would have nothing to fear. Or have lions just failed to catch some drinking animals, and are they still lurking somewhere in the grass? In that case baboons will be the next victims.

A strange thing now happens. The observer has the impression that the baboons are behaving as if not one of them is willing to admit that he is afraid. They behave as if they were not thirsty in the least. They romp and play games in the branches of the last trees. But every now and then a courageous baboon makes a dash in the direction of the water-hole and then turns back. Each time he goes a little farther towards it.

He takes a short rest in the tree-tops to recover his breath, and then makes another dash, obviously intent on reaching the water-hole this time, but before he gets there three lionesses simultaneously leap towards him. He slips agilely between two of them, and a moment later has reached the safety of a tree, where a whole family of lions tries to jump up and reach him.

An infernal din breaks out among the baboons in the tree-tops. The bravest descend from the trees and behave as if they are about to make a most ferocious attack on the lions, but always turn back at a safe distance. Other baboons break off branches and throw them about in blind fury. After some time the lions seem to realise that they are not going to get anywhere. Besides, the din made by the apes is frightening off all the other animals that want to reach the water-hole. So there is nothing for it but to give up and try their luck at another water-hole or in the open plain, leaving the baboons to drink in peace.

Wars Between Baboon States?

Soon afterwards five elephants and two rhinoceroses appear on the scene, but the baboons do not worry about them. If one of these colossi happens to come close to a baboon, it moves aside a yard or so, reluctantly and only at the last moment, rather like a pedestrian getting out of the way of a steam-roller.

A little while later another troop of baboons turns up. The two troops appear to know each other well. Even so, they watch each other with interest. They make way for each other, so that everyone has his turn. The two troops drink and play unconcernedly side by side, but no baboon ever mingles with the other group. The invisible frontier is strictly preserved, and any inexperienced child who seems about to cross it is brought back immediately.

The meaning of this behaviour is clear. If some quite trifling cause, such as a squabble about a tuft of grass, led to a clash between two strange baboons between whom no order of precedence had been established, a minor 'border conflict' might quickly expand into all-out war between the two baboon 'nations'. Such wars have sometimes been described to Europeans by natives. They are extremely rare, however, and arise, not from aggressive intentions, but from the 'law' that makes baboons go to the assistance of hard-pressed members of their group.

Their peaceable nature is illustrated by the fact that a troop of baboons may regard as its own a territory of about four square miles with several water-holes. If a strange baboon troop wants to march through its territory or use a water-hole, as frequently happens, permission is never refused. Wars of conquest between baboon states are unthinkable.

The two American scientists, as we mentioned above, were able to make all these observations only because they managed to procure themselves something like naturalisation into the baboon community.

It is easy enough to go by car to numerous nature reserves in Africa where baboons abound. They lie in wait on the roads, climb on the radiator and beg for food, often threateningly. It is just as well to shut the windows to avoid their importunities. These ape highwaymen are, however, entirely unsuitable for study of baboon life in natural conditions. But tracking down one of the few baboon troops still living in such conditions is extraordinarily difficult. They are so shy of human beings that it is generally impossible even to photograph them with a telephoto lens. But on the East African plains a fleeing troop can be followed in a cross-country vehicle until it stops in exhaustion. If the right tactics are adopted, the baboons quickly realise that no danger threatens from this vehicle and its occupants. Slowly they grow friendly, and after a certain probationary period allow human beings to walk about among them unmolested.

Professor Washburn and Dr. DeVore generally kept at some distance from them, however, so as not to interfere with the course of natural events by their presence. But future students ought to take part in the life of these creatures, and above all study their language. It is now known how they make friends, and with what lip-smacking sounds a female offers herself to a male. The characteristic sounds have been identified that are used to report the presence of leopards, as well as the rather different sounds that give warning of prowling lions. Long conversations have been overheard in which the animals, with almost human grunting sounds, smacking of lips and lively gestures, communicated to each other what were evidently matters of great interest. Yet the meaning of these conversations remains totally obscure.

A step towards the interpretation of ape language was taken in an experiment carried out at the Bronx Zoo, New York, early in 1962. The chatter of apes in an open reserve was recorded while threatening thunderclouds were gathering. Later, on a fine, sunny day, the tape was played back to them. At first the animals were taken aback. Then they dashed to shelter from the rain they thought was coming. This demonstrates that apes possess a regular sound language and understood their earlier 'weather talks' when reproduced through a loudspeaker.

Bushmen in the Kalahari desert speak in much the same way, almost exclusively with click and grunt sounds, which are produced partly in the stomach and chest, and they, too, help themselves out with hand and finger movements and by highly expressive pantomime. So it comes as no surprise that Jens Bjerre, a Dane who in 1957 lived for six months among these people in the Kalahari, should speak of an old bushman who maintained that he could imitate the language of baboons in every detail of gesture and sound and converse regularly with them.

Baboon Goat-herd

This chapter cannot be concluded without reference to the observations made in 1961 at Okahandje in South-West Africa by Dr. Walter Hoesch, the internationally known German zoologist, shortly before a heart attack put an end to his strenuous life.

He made a thorough study of the behaviour of a female baboon that worked on a farm as – goat-herd.

That sounds like a newspaper stunt, but is nevertheless a fact worthy of serious scientific study, as is vouched for by the accounts published in reputable scientific journals such as the *Zeitschrift für Tierpsychologie* and the *Naturwissenschaftliche Rundschau*.

Ahla, a female baboon on the Otjiruse farm near Windhuk, takes about eighty goats out to graze every day, and does so without any human escort or supervision. She is by no means exceptional, having had two predecessors in her job, one of whom carried it out to the complete satisfaction of her employer for fully six years.

Mrs. Aston, the owner of the farm, asked why she used apes for this purpose, explained that she grew tired of the losses of grazing animals that occurred when she employed native goat-herds. Nearly every evening some animals were missing, having strayed or been scattered by beasts of prey. Employing an ape had put an end to all this. The herd reached the drinking-trough in the evening complete, led by Ahla with her 'ho-ho-ho' call. As for the kids, she never allowed a mistake to occur in matching up mother and child, a thing which was constantly happening before with Mrs. Aston's Ovambos.

Female baboons did not need to be trained for their responsibilities. Ahla had been caught by a native at the age of two, and was then kept for three days in a special compartment of the goat kraal in company with the new-born kids, and was fed on goat's milk.

She soon began following the herd when it went out to pasture in the morning. On the very first occasion, without being shown by anyone what to do or how to do it, she made vocal contact with the goats and maintained it without interruption until returning home in the evening. She noticed immediately if any goats were missing, having perhaps gone to rest in the shade of a bush. When this happened she jumped on the back of a big goat or climbed a tree, rapidly surveyed the landscape, and then fetched the runaways back to the herd with cries and smacks. Incidentally, she never guided the herd, but only accompanied it. The direction was always decided by the goats themselves.

The only thing Mrs Aston had to teach her was that she must not take young kids under her arm and climb trees with them just for the fun of it. There was, however, no objection to one privilege Ahla granted herself. As soon as she believed herself to be out of sight of the farm, she jumped on one of the goats, always the same one, and rode it.

In a few days she knew all eighty goats personally. If Mrs. Aston bought a new goat and wished to include it in the herd, she first had to introduce it to Ahla. Otherwise she would have driven it away unmercifully.

Only Mistake

One morning, half an hour after leaving the farm, Ahla came back in a great fluster, full of growls and complaints. Whatever was the matter with her? The Ovambo who milked the goats had forgotten to let out two kids which had gone out grazing for the first time on the previous day. When Mrs. Aston discovered what had happened and had the two kids let out, Ahla promptly took charge and led them safely to the herd.

About one of the ape's quite remarkable capacities Dr. Hoesch writes as follows: 'When Ahla comes home from pasture in the evening with the herd, first of all she drinks at the trough together with the goats. Then she goes to the kraal, from where she climbs through a skylight into the walled kid kraal. From there she cannot see the herd of grown animals, but can only hear them. During the space of about an hour that follows, the animals drift one by one back to the main kraal.

'Whenever she hears the voice of a mother bleating for her kid, she picks out the right kid, jumps through the skylight with it, and puts it to its mother's udder. Even when several adult goats are bleating at the same time and several kids are answering, she never makes a mistake. She actually takes young kids to their mothers before they have made vocal contact.

'She recognises every animal in the herd, but how she does so remains a riddle. . . . No native or white man would be capable of picking out the right kid out of twenty or more, often of the same colour and age, and giving it to the right mother. But Ahla is infallible.

'The zeal she displays in putting the kids to the maternal udder borders on mania. She can never bide her time. Once all the kids are with the mothers, she supervises the feeding, and frequently puts back to the udder kids that are satisfied and have left the mother. When the kids' legs are still weak, she supports them. If the mother still has a lot of milk left after the kid's hunger is appeased, she sucks some out, though otherwise she never pilfers.

'The only mistake she ever made was this. If Mrs. Aston, when a goat had given birth to three kids, removed one of them to have it reared by a mother that had only one, Ahla invariably fetched it back again, no matter where it had been taken.

'She carries home under her arm kids that are born out at grazing.

'This exercise of the maternal instinct on an alien species

seems to me especially noteworthy. Young baboons are not carried, but cling fast to the breast hair-covering, which kids cannot do. Ahla appreciates the situation, and acts otherwise than she would have done in the baboon herd, and she does not do what her present herd companions do in such cases. Mother goat and kid stay out the first night after a birth if no one is there to take the kid home.'

Ahla, who feeds herself out at pasture, received no recompense for her work, so that there is no question of indirect training.

Are this animal's actions governed by the first beginnings of reason?

8

THE PECKING ORDER

Etiquette in the Farmyard

NEARLY all the animals that live apparently at peace in larger or smaller communities with their own kind present a picture of blissful harmony – the poultry-yard, the dove-cot, the herd of cows, the flock of blackbirds, the troop of baboons and the 'urban' community of prairie-dogs. Similar communities exist among wolves, crocodiles, crabs in a river, bats in a ruin, crickets on a mound, fish and many other creatures.

But such peace is possible only after they have bitten or pecked out for themselves a fixed and unequivocal order of precedence from the most powerful male to the weakest female.

Without this order of precedence, without the preliminary trial of strength that demonstrates once and for all what the outcome of any dispute between two individuals would be, there would be no such peaceful co-existence. Squabbles over food and the desire for the most comfortable sleeping quarters would lead to perpetual disturbances of the peace. The order of precedence establishes a code of behaviour that avoids all that. How it all works has been established in recent years by patient and protracted observation.

It is poor testimony to man's powers of observation that research into this situation has been going on only for fifty years. The fowl has been domesticated for thousands of years, but it was only about forty years ago that the pecking order in the poultry-yard was discovered by the Norwegian Thorleif Schelderup-Ebbe. One of the many scientists in this field now is Dr. Erich Baeumer, a non-resident member of the Max Planck Institute for Physiology of Behaviour at Seewiesen, near Munich, who has devoted himself in the past few years to the task of drawing up a detailed book of farmyard etiquette.

The first signs of the instincts that make the pecking order necessary appear in chicks at the age of three weeks. Curiously enough, they are very marked in incubator-hatched chicks which are subsequently reared largely in separate pens.

These cheeping little tufts of feathers have never seen a clucking hen or other adult fowl that might possibly have taught them behaviour. Nevertheless they conduct their trials of strength exactly like naturally hatched chicks.

The scene seems cheerful and innocent enough. The three-week chicks run about picking grains of corn. If two happen to meet, they may momentarily adopt what are evidently fighting attitudes. A little while later one of them, still quite play-fully, takes a peck with his beak. The other falls back in dismay.

If the incident is repeated two or three times more, the chick that falls back is stamped as inferior to the other, perhaps for its whole life-time. Thus among chicks of the same age a pecking order can be established playfully and almost without a struggle.

But this happy state of affairs does not last for long. These infantile clashes leave many obscurities in the pecking order still unresolved. If, for instance, two chicks meet and neither gives way, in default of an actual fight the issue is left open.

Thus all sorts of inflammable matter is bottled up in the chicks until they reach the age of about seven weeks, when they have grown quite strong, and it suddenly flares up in all the chicks in a pen at the same time. When the first two chicks go for each other in earnest, the contagion immediately spreads throughout the pen. Every chick seems to realise that its whole future is at stake, and that what it fails to do now can never be made good.

In a moment the whole pen is full of scuffling couples. A beaten chick must immediately measure itself with another, and the winner promptly seeks out another and stronger opponent. Every chick 'pecks itself up as high as it can'. But they always fight fair. Two chicks never attack one chick at the same time.

The hardest struggles naturally take place at the top. Ultimately all the chicks are drenched and spattered with blood, and the fight ends in general exhaustion. During the next two or three days the winners exploit their triumph to the full and bully the weaker chickens, but they soon feel secure, and quiet returns – and lasts for a very long time.

Victory does not always go to brute force. Just as often it is the reward of endurance, adroitness, impudence or good nerves. It pays to be quicker than one's opponent in recovering from the shock of a peck received, and to be ready to fight again before he is. Sometimes, indeed, victory goes to a swaggerer with feathers ruffled up if his opponent allows himself to be bluffed and intimidated and beats a retreat before the first peck. Bluffers have just as good prospects in the poultry-yard as they have in human society.

A crucial factor may be whether the feathered combatant happens to be in form or not on the great day. Also the sight of a delectable morsel may distract him at a critical moment and lead to swift and unexpected defeat, from which recovery is hardly possible.

If the fight takes place in the open yard in the presence of adult fowl, as a rule the latter intervene with a great deal of cackling. They thus influence the outcome in a far from satisfactory manner, as they unintentionally assist to victory chicks that have not deserved it. These sometimes lead to complications and illogicalities in the pecking order.

Among the female adults in one poultry-yard, for instance, it was observed that while No. 1 chased No. 2 away from the feeding-place, and No. 2 dealt with No. 3 in the same way, No. 3 always chased away No. 1.

Erich Baeumer tells the following story that illustrates the complicated conditions that can arise in the farmyard even among such primitive creatures as fowl.

The top female in his yard was the hen Anna. One day a piece of fence separating his yard from his neighbour's collapsed, and Anna at once exploited her opportunity of extending her sphere of influence. She promptly fell in with Cleopatra, the neighbour's top-ranking fowl, and defeated her. She also overthrew the No. 2 hen, and should thus really have become the mistress of the whole territory. But things turned out otherwise.

Next day she went back to the neighbour's yard and was about to give a dressing-down to an unruly fowl of low rank when the enemy cock appeared between them like a *deus ex machina*. Anna panicked and took to flight, and in her agitation missed the gap in the fence and fell among strange fowl; so cowed was she that she put up no resistance, and allowed herself to be harried by them just as they pleased. Henceforward she was indeed able to command respect from Cleopatra and her deputy, but had to knuckle under to all the weaker fowl, and only managed to repair the check to her prestige in a protracted series of single combats.

She was able to do this only because she was notably superior to the other hens. Minor injustices in the order of precedence cannot be corrected, and remain as they were established once and for all, however unfairly that may have been.

Teenage Revolt

A furtive revolt always takes place in the farmyard when a new generation of young cocks reaches 'teenage' and they increasingly feel the need to assert themselves against the regiment of women. To do this they have to establish their precedence in separate combat with each adult hen.

The outcome of these encounters varies greatly. Many chicken lose their nerve at the mere sight of the 'cock face' and the fiery comb and take to flight, screeching loudly, at the cock's first or second spring. Others are quite unimpressed by the pose and the dilated ruff and sharply attack and defeat the cockerel, who then has to defer his ambition for weeks; or else they are defeated by him after a hard fight.

The cockerel is nearly always chivalrous in victory. In a favourable position he will refrain from giving a painful bite and wait to see if his female opponent does not of her own accord recognise the hopelessness of her position and give in. Sometimes he will pay court to her after defeating her. In that case, instead of running away she stoops for mating.

There are, however, chicken who cannot get over being defeated by much younger cockerels. Erich Baeumer tells of his bantam hen Minette, who in anticipation of threats to come used on every possible occasion to attack quite small cockerels like a fury and scatter them in all directions, in order to impress respect on the youngsters and intimidate them in good time.

When the cockerels grew bigger and were as much as a hand taller than the bantam, Minette's preventive war against them assumed grotesque forms. She would retire into an ambush, lie in wait until a cockerel came past, and then pounce on the unsuspecting creature. If the cockerel were startled and ran off cackling, she would stand there for a few moments in a victorious pose, trembling with excitement, but soon relapsed into insecurity and again made for a secret corner. One day, however, she met her match and short shrift was made of her.

Sometimes a young male has by no means an easy task in asserting himself if his owner wishes to establish him as the new cock of the walk. One such unfortunate was Pasha, who quickly achieved supremacy over all the fowls except Alma, the No. 1 among them, who warded off all his attacks by the most violent pecking. But when spring came the warfare between them ceased, and they became a loving couple. Whenever Pasha called she came obediently, and his supremacy seemed undisputed.

But no sooner was the honeymoon over than Alma grew refractory again. Pasha grew much stronger than she, but that did not save him from a beating up whenever he tried feebly remonstrating with her. So it went on, day after day. It took him a long time to pluck up his courage, but one day, when it looked as if Alma was going to put him in his place as usual, he at last really asserted himself, and with spurs and beak made it plain who was master of the house.

Magnanimity in Victory

When full-grown cocks come into conflict, things are more serious. They observe strict routine in their combats.

They begin by strutting towards each other, crowing and flapping their wings. Then they circle round each other several times and finally come to rest facing each other, four inches apart, with lowered heads. Each searches out the other's weakness, and then suddenly, as if at a gong-stroke, both leap high into the air, each trying to leap higher than the other so as to belabour him with his spurs and peck at him violently. If both reach the same height simultaneously, they collide, neither has the advantage, the first round is over, and the second can begin.

After four or five jumps, both are winded, struggle noisily for breath and utter piercing complaints. Their red combs change to a bluish shade. At this point it may be tactically advisable to miss a jump, husband one's strength and concentrate on defence, so as to get the better of one's opponent next time. The best defence is to dodge backwards or to left or right, according to the way one's opponent jumps, or to duck down forward very low. If the consequence is that one's opponent leaps into the void, his impetus may easily cause him to fall upside down on his back – a disgrace which seriously impairs his fighting spirit. If the party on the defensive is unable to avoid his opponent's leap, he protects his head by drawing it well in behind his two wings, which he raises high, like shields.

There is no limit to the number of rounds. The fight goes on until one or other concedes defeat by taking to flight. If he is in a corner from which he cannot flee, he indicates his

SOME SCENES IN THE POULTRY-YARD

1. Introductory crossing of beaks at the beginning of the fray. 2. The feathers begin to fly. 3. End of the battle. The loser on his knees. 4. A cockerel has vanquished the bantam hen Minette. She gives in; he spares her. 5. A clucking hen successfully defends her feeding-ground against a hen of superior rank. 6. A timely ducking motion by the cock on the right causes its opponent to turn a somersault and fall backwards. 7. 'Mistaken' hiding of heads by both cocks behind wings drawn up like shields. 8. Ducking sideways with eyes shut. The jumper is more agile than the one in drawing No. 6, and keeps his balance. 9. Defeated cock gives the signal for capitulation by hiding his head in a hole. 10. Defeated hen flaps her wings and thus makes it known that she has resigned herself to her position and does not wish to renew the struggle. 11. By bowing his head and raising his wings the defeated cock (*left*) intimates to his former rival that he will in future respect the latter's position of precedence. 12. After defeat a cock hides in a dark corner and spends a few days mourning there with dishevelled plumage.

capitulation by pressing his head into the corner or, better still, into a box, pail or dark hole. While in this humble posture not a feather of his is touched by the victor, who remains on the spot for a little while and then goes on his way.

But the cock who has struck his flag usually hides his head in his corner for half an hour without moving, long after the victor has departed. The humiliation is evidently keenly felt, for after defeat cocks — and hens too — 'mourn', often for hours or days on end. They retire to the loneliest and darkest place possible and remain there almost motionless in an attitude of abject misery.

It is pitiful to see the first encounters between winner and loser after the mourning period is over. Defeated cocks shrink into themselves and begin to cackle as only hens do otherwise. With fowls the effect of an embarrassed shrug of the shoulders is given by a feeble flapping of both wings two or three times in succession.

This indicates that they have resigned themselves to defeat.

The top-ranking animals are well-fed, sleek and self-confident. They are affable rather than tyrannical in their attitude to the lower ranks.

Sometimes a 'lady' of the upper classes picks out a girl friend from the lower classes, and loads her with proofs of her affection, and the latter then impudently ventures to take liberties with others. Manifestations of friendship in the poultry-yard include nestling in the neck plumage or 'full dress', the 'lady' passing her friend's damp or soiled feathers delicately through her beak, while the latter keeps still with eyes closed in contentment.

Fowl assist one another in certain situations. If one of them has a long, woody stalk stuck in its throat, for instance, it need only draw attention to itself, and another fowl will immediately come and extract it.

Inferiority Complex

Fowl of the lower social grades look dirty and cowed. Wherever they go they are likely to be driven off with pecks, and this applies particularly to places where there is good food or other amenities. This makes them decidedly quarrelsome and irascible to the few still lower in the social order than themselves.

It is on the latter that they work off their 'inferiority complex', and they usually do so within seconds of having been humiliated by a superior. They make a bee-line for a social inferior, and attack her like a bolt from the blue, jumping up on her and tearing out her feathers.

Awkward situations may arise, however, for if the victim of this aggression notices her assailant and jumps aside, the assailant shoots past her into the void, with head high in warlike pose. If, however, a higher-ranking fowl happens to be standing by, the fowl thus working off her inferiority complex has promptly to apologise if she wishes to avoid punishment. The gesture of apology consists in bending the head, a fawning, sideways motion and a slight raising of both wings as she turns away. In most cases the apology is accepted.

Fish Discipline

Are there other 'badges of rank' in the animal world apart from a spruce or unkempt appearance, nutritional condition and self-confidence? On the west coast of India and Ceylon the Giant Danio or *Danio Malabaricus* lives in small communities of about ten. Each school occupies a definite area, which it defends against invasion by others of the species, and in each there is a strict order of precedence. Young fish of the same age settle things between themselves by swimming races, or sometimes by ramming or fin-beating matches. The senior member of the group maintains the normal horizontal position in the water, but his juniors adopt 'posture' in his presence. 'Posture' is a sloping position, head up, tail down. The lower the rank, the steeper the slope. Professor Adolf Haas measured it with a protractor, with these results:

First in rank	0 degrees	Fourth	38 degrees
Second	20 degrees	Fifth	41 degrees
Third	32 degrees	Sixth	43 degrees

Thus the biggest differences are among the seniors. From the sixth fish downwards the angular differences are almost imperceptible.

Discipline is strictly enforced. At frequent intervals the

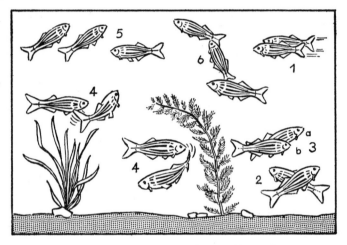

STRUGGLES FOR PRECEDENCE AMONG GIANT DANIOS

1. Two fish determine their order of precedence by engaging in a swimming race. The winner leading by a head. 2. During a pause in the race two opponents of equal rank use criss-cross motions to impress. The result is still open. 3. During the struggle the superior (*a*) shows the inferior (*b*) the oblique attitude he must adopt in future. 4. The senior admonishes the incorrect behaviour of inferiors by a blow on the head with its fin. 5. Two inferiors rise when the senior approaches. 6. The weakest member of a group normally inclining at an angle of 45 degrees is so intimidated by the passage above and below it of senior fish that it inclines at an angle of 60 degrees.

senior fish makes a tour of inspection to ensure there are no infringements. A fish that out of self-assertion or negligence claims too high a rank and does not slope, or makes an error of only one degree, receives a vigorous stroke of the fin. The Danios fear this and, if caught unawares by the approach of the inspecting officer, often tilt more steeply than their rank requires. As soon as authority, and with it the fright, has disappeared, they return to their proper angle.

Swagger Can Pay

Back now to the poultry-yard, where differences in rank are so finely shaded as to be evident in detail only to the fowl themselves.

Erich Baeumer went about classifying his fowl in order of precedence as follows. First of all he tried the food trick, as described earlier in the case of the baboons. But this failed with fowl, because of their 'slowness in the uptake'.

So he picked up each fowl in turn and thrust it against another as if it were about to peck it. When this is done the senior animals ignore the man holding the fowl and vent their anger on the junior. They assume an offensive position and try to peck back. Junior animals, however, turn timidly away. This can be taken advantage of to vary the pecking order at will.

The experimenter, for instance, takes the 'top' fowl while an assistant takes a fowl of inferior grade, and the two are held close to the ground and a sort of mock fight is made to take place between the two in which they in reality only play the part of puppets. If the 'top' fowl is continually withdrawn when the inferior fowl is pushed at it, the 'prima donna' ends by acquiring an inferiority complex, while the one-time Cinderella develops megalomania. When they are left to themselves again the unnatural relationship that has been forced on them remains unchanged for a long time. Its place in the pecking order can have a surprising effect on the creature's intelligence. A lower place invariably makes it more stupid than it is by nature.

Its intelligence can be tested by measuring the speed with which it can be taught certain tricks. Dr. Diebschlag, who was killed in the last war, carried out the following experiment.

He took two birds from a pigeon-loft, each of which, when tested separately, displayed exactly the same ability to learn. When they were put together in the test cage, however, the 'subordinate' bird promptly showed a considerable reduction in ability. In the presence of its senior it became stupid.

But that was not all. Dr. Diebschlag decked out the inferior pigeon with imposing 'war paint'; he gave it a martial appearance with paint and extra tufts of feathers. The stronger pigeon was completely taken in by this bluff, and took second place without a struggle. In the ensuing intelligence tests it behaved like a dunce, while the other bird did excellently, in spite of its previous below-average performance.

Thus swagger can pay off in animals as in man. As we have already mentioned, by ruffling its feathers, spreading out its ruff, stretching, making the comb redden and swell, and by cackling, a fowl can gain a higher rank than is its due. The clucking of hens provides a striking example of this. The emergence of the maternal instinct can turn a low-grade hen into a bumptious, tyrannical, mettlesome tyrant overnight.

The exceptional and privileged position granted spontaneously by baboons to 'mothers with children' is not granted spontaneously in the farmyard; hens have to win it for themselves by putting on airs and making a noise. Disregard of their position results in such furious attack that others keep at a respectful distance. They keep a sharp look-out for any fowl who has ever molested one of their straying chicks. The malefactor is attacked furiously from behind and feathers are made to fly.

Male into Female

Strange situations may develop from the pecking order in some bird species, pigeons and common ravens, for instance. In a pigeon-house the number of males and females may be roughly equal, but all the males do not lord it over all the females. Many weakly cock-pigeons are far inferior in rank to the most pugnacious females.

When love comes to the pigeon-house, a formidable Amazon will frequently pair off with a narrow-chested male. In such a case the 'lady' will importune the 'gentleman' with an ostentatious display of the kind reserved for the male in the pigeon book of etiquette. The weakling accepts the role thus thrust upon him and crouches before her in a most effeminate fashion, and the loving couple coo tenderly in roles reversed, incapable of fulfilling their biological function.

Professor Konrad Lorenz, of the Max Planck Institute for Physiology of Behaviour at Seewiesen, near Munich, reports the following: 'I had four common ravens, an old couple which was just preparing for a brood, and two young females. At first I took it that these two young females were a couple, as they made noisy mating-calls, the male role always falling to the elder and stronger of the two sisters. The old couple had a failure with the brood, and the male finally drove the female away for good and all. When I put the two young ravens with him, to my surprise the sister I had previously regarded as a male welcomed the male's advances, and the two became a couple.

'I was especially interested to note that this female did not desist at once from her masculine courtship of her sister. She acted simultaneously as female to the old male and as male to her little sister. Not until she was definitely established as the mate of the old male did she begin to show hostility to her sister as a potential rival.'

9

DEGENERATION OF
COMMUNITY LIFE

Unhappy Paradise

IN 1954 Dr. John B. Calhoun carried out a remarkable experiment on rats at Palo Alto, near San Francisco.

He shut up twenty male and twenty female rats in a 1,000-square-yard enclosure in conditions which should have represented a rats' earthly paradise. They were given an abundance of excellent food, water for all their needs, nest-building materials in unlimited quantities. They had no enemies to fear, and a veterinary surgeon saw to it that there was no outbreak of disease. They were able to eat and drink and multiply to their hearts' content.

After twenty-seven months they ought to have increased in number to about 5,000 – there was ample space and food – but instead the population numbered only 150 grown rats, a number which did not change appreciably in later months.

How is this to be explained? It turns out that growth of population in an animal species is restricted not only by privation, disease and food shortage, but also by a psychological phenomenon – the degeneration of community life resulting from over-population.

Dr. Calhoun devised this experiment to show how the community life of rats deteriorates with increasing density of population to the point at which cannibalism sets in.

He built four identical enclosures in a row in the laboratory. Each was a complete and self-sufficient living area with food bowls, water-trough, storage places, nest-building materials and five nest-boxes. The latter were arranged in tiers and were easily accessible by a spiral stairway. More food was always available than the animals could consume.

The special feature of the arrangement lay in three bridges by which the rats could pass from Enclosure 1 to Enclosure 2, on to Enclosures 3 and 4 and back the same way. These bridges were so narrow that only one animal could pass at a time.

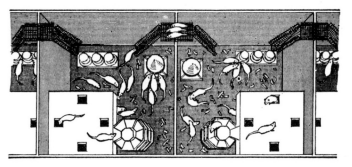

View of sections 2 and 3 of the experimental rat enclosure.

This was an ideal arrangement for demonstrating automatic shifts of population.

In two enclosures conditions remained normal and healthy, while in the other two conditions set in leading in the direction of the destruction of the breed.

What happened was this. As soon as young rats reached maturity at six months a succession of battles for precedence began in each enclosure, conducted according to strict rules, as previously described. In principle it is the same phenomenon as the struggle for precedence among young fowl.

The outcome was that in the two end enclosures, Nos. 1 and 4, a male rat established himself as dictator and harem-sultan. The defeated males, however, were not driven out. On the contrary, something very peculiar happened.

While the sultan, savouring his omnipotence, had a good long sleep every morning, the defeated males had to get up early, for this was the only time when they could eat and drink in peace, unmolested by him.

As we have mentioned, there was food in abundance in their own enclosure. But rats are impelled by instinct to fetch their food from a distance, whether the latter be short or long. So they disregarded their own well-filled food bowl and chased each other over the bridge to eat in the next enclosure.

Sometimes they dawdled, and when they wanted to go home the sultan would be awake and would prevent them from returning. He kept watch on the bridge and even made his bed there. Usually when lying at the foot of the bridge he kept his eyes shut and slept, or at any rate pretended to. If one of his harem came scampering over the bridge from the next enclosure he seemed to take no notice, but slept on.

But if a male came cautiously sneaking across and thrust his head ever so slightly over the top, the sultan would see him, and he needed only to give a tired blink from one eye-slit to send the intruder flying.

The sultan tolerates a few other males in his kingdom, but these are always the weakest, most submissive and spineless animals. He is even able to leave them alone with his harem, confident in the knowledge that they will give him no cause for jealousy.

Thus in the two end enclosures, both of which had of course only one bridge, everything went on its normal and orderly course. The females had many young, infant mortality was relatively low and the unwanted surplus young were ejected into the next enclosure.

In the two middle enclosures, which had two bridges, the state of affairs was totally different. No male ever succeeded in establishing supremacy. If he stood guard at one bridge, intruders entered by the other. Thus stability could never be reached.

In these enclosures the density of population rapidly increased. In particular, there was a concentration of defeated males who had migrated from the end enclosures, and at the same time a shortage of females. In the end enclosures a sultan might, for instance, rule over two slaves and a harem of from seven to ten females. In the middle enclosures there would be only ten females to twenty or thirty males.

Peculiar Eating Habits

As the number of animals increased in the middle enclosures the first symptoms of deterioration appeared. The first were strange eating habits. Normally a rat will eat grain several times a day, whenever it feels hungry.

Eating, however, became more and more neurotic. With the growth of population the rats ate less and less often, though the food bowls were filled up before their eyes and there was nothing to prevent access to them. But no sooner did one animal run to the bowl and begin to eat than all the others wanted to eat too, and all out of the same trough. Sometimes they would jostle and bite each other to get at it, while just beside them a second bowl remained unheeded and untouched.

Thus an atmosphere of nervous exasperation developed. During the long hours of the day in which no animal dared eat because no other was eating, they kept a sharp look-out on each other to make sure no one was taking the first step. Thus they all increasingly neglected their other activities.

In this general state of nerves the first thing to suffer was the nest-building instinct. Normally male and female build a nest together. The female does this with much greater devotion during the gestation period. The animals carried scraps of paper piece by piece from a store by way of the spiral stairway into their wooden nest-box. There they arranged the strips to form a soft, warm cavity.

When over-population set in the males dropped out of sharing in the housework, but the females too ceased caring about shaping the nest properly. They would merely pile the strips of paper in a heap and jump on them two or three times, as if that were good enough to make a proper nest.

Under still greater pressure of population the females grew lazier and lazier. They would simply drop the paper strips and begin doing something else, generally something suggested

123

by a meeting with other rats. The nest padding grew thinner and thinner, the bed for the young harder and harder. In the end nests were no longer built at all, and the young were born on the bare wood of the nest-boxes.

A further symptom of degeneration appeared in the treatment of the young. When rat mothers living in regular conditions scent danger, they carry their young one after another in their mouth to a place they consider safe. Nothing, even a threat to their own life, deters them from this, until the last of the litter is in a safe place.

In conditions of stress, of over-population, however, they began neglecting this. In case of danger – they could be deluded into scenting danger by a tape-recording of dogs barking – they put away only some of their young. They even forgot where they put them, and left them lying about all over the place, just dumping them like the scraps of paper, and they failed to bring them back to the nest when the danger was over.

Thus in quite a short time all the young of a litter would be scattered senselessly all over the enclosure. Their mother would feed them rarely, or not at all, in spite of their piteous squeaking. They died where they were abandoned, and were then eaten by some passing male.

Disorganisation of Marital Life

Marital life, too, was grotesquely disrupted. Rat courtships normally take the following course. A male pursues the female of his choice. She carries out a kind of sham flight and retires into her nest. The suitor waits patiently outside, only sticking his nose inside occasionally, perhaps just to announce that he is still there. Rat etiquette forbids him to enter. Instead he performs a ritual courtship dance, accompanied by squeaking and whistling. Finally the courted female emerges and accepts his wooing.

After degeneration set in, things were altogether different. No sooner did a female in heat appear than she was unmercifully pursued by a swarm of savage, importunate males, and there was no escaping their attentions. If she succeeded in retreating into her nest, several males, heedless of the taboo, followed her in. Such incidents in unbroken succession have the most serious consequences for the females. Their instinctual life is disrupted. Most become incapable of carrying the young to full time, or do not survive parturition.

Even the wives of the two sultans in the end enclosures, where an orderly life still prevailed, suffered in consequence. They often made excursions into the over-populated middle enclosures where they had no protection from their sultan. Thus there was no immoderate increase in the numbers of these harem ladies.

The males also were not spared abnormal changes in instinctual behaviour. With the progressive over-population two distinct character-types emerged. The first were the 'eccentrics', who lived in pathological seclusion, slept by day and were wide awake only for a while at night. They ran about, ate and drank only when their fellows were asleep.

The other, more numerous, type were the 'hysterics', who bustled about feverishly all day long, and totally ignored all previously established rules of precedence. They showed superior males no respect and returned to the attack if driven off by them – which usually ended with the death of one or the other. These hysterics ended by becoming cannibals. They ignored all combat rules, fought to the death and ate the loser.

The outcome of all this was an infant mortality rate of 96 per cent, a maternal mortality rate of more than 50 per cent and the premature death of most of the males, if not in battle, from psychological depression, debilitation or exhaustion. It was by no means rare for the whole group of rats to be wiped out. Even if a normal density of population was regained, normal conditions did not reappear.

10

ANIMAL LANGUAGES

Talking to Geese

WHEN crows caw, geese cackle, nightingales sing, crickets chirp or foxes whine, the meaning of these sounds is unintelligible to us. It need not always be so. Scientists in many countries are beginning to decipher animal languages, thus realising a long-cherished dream of mankind. They have already succeeded in conversing with geese and grasshoppers. Professor Konrad Lorenz has succeeded in interpreting the language of geese. An unbroken cackle or bursts of cackle of more than six syllables, something like 'ga, ga, ga, ga, ga, ga, ga' means: 'We feel comfortable here. There's plenty to eat. Let us stay.'

If the burst of cackle has only six syllables, it means 'The meadow grass is poor. Let us nibble at a blade here and there and waddle on slowly, in low gear, so to speak.' Five syllables mean: 'Move into second gear.' Four syllables mean: 'Get into third gear, stretch neck forward.' Three syllables mean: 'Waddle as fast as possible. Keep on the alert. We are probably about to take off.'

If it is desired to intimate the intention of waddling as fast as possible but not taking off, the trisyllabic 'ga, ga, ga' is replaced by a 'ga, gi, ga' on a high middle note. To an initiate into goose-language it sounds strange when the white house goose, which has lost the capacity for flight, emphasises the fact that it has no intention of taking off by eagerly reiterating 'ga, gi, ga'. So deeply is speech-behaviour anchored in its heredity that the 'idiom' inherited from the wild goose has outlived the capacity to fly.

The alarm signal of geese, if, say, a dog approaches, is a.

single, not very loud, rather nasal-sounding 'ra', which causes the whole company to take off with a great flapping of wings. The 'all clear' is a low, continuous cackle.

Konrad Lorenz made such friends with a flock of geese that he came to be accepted as a fellow-member of the breed, though a rather odd-looking one. His language studies were not so simple, however, notably because of the difficulties of the hoarseness-producing pronunciation and the furious pace of the cackling. But he succeeded in communicating with the geese, and managed to get them to slow down or accelerate their waddling speed at will.

The example of these geese illustrates the fact that in the case of many creatures the function of language is not communication in our sense of the word. They emit a kind of music with a strong emotional colouring depending on their mood, and thus transmit their psychological state to their fellows, in so far as these have an appropriate 'receiver' with which to pick it up.

This, however, does certainly not apply to the whole animal kingdom, for there are animals that use their capacity for communication deliberately, and sometimes with a calculated and cunning purpose. We need only recall baboons and porpoises, and the fact that dogs enjoy hoodwinking their masters.

Crows' Dialects

Curiously enough, the language of many creatures – the cawing of crows, for instance – is not intelligible to their kind all over the world. Sometimes a Babylonian confusion of tongues prevails, for different dialects have developed in different continents and countries.

On this point Professor Hubert Frings of Pennsylvania University made a surprising observation. Just as an Upper Bavarian peasant who all his life has hardly left his native village with the best will in the world cannot understand a fisherman from the North Sea coast who speaks Low German, so are there 'provincial' crows who never meet other species

of their kind on their wanderings. They do not even under
stand the 'alarm' call of a strange crow, and when they hear
it they stay where they are instead of making for safety.

There are also more cosmopolitan crows, however. On their
migrations in spring and autumn they meet other flocks of
crows and learn their dialects. They even master the most
important features of the jackdaw and gull languages.

This marked linguistic skill enables widely travelled crows,
those of one eastern American species, for instance, to understand at the first caw European crows whose 'dialect' they have
never previously heard. In protracted experiments, in which
he was aided by his wife, Professor Frings established that
'provincial' crows are not capable of this until they have
attended the 'international crow language school' for at least a
year.

So far about 300 different utterances by crows have been
identified, the great majority of which have of course not yet
been interpreted. An uninterrupted caw on a specially hoarse
note is a summons to all the members of the flock to assemble
in a field.

To listen in to what takes place at these assemblies, Professor Frings hid a number of microphones and loudspeakers in
a cornfield. Whenever a flock flew past he sounded the
assembly call from a tape-recorder. Only after many attempts
did he have any luck; a flock of crows was taken in by the
voice on the loudspeaker and touched down.

There was such a confusion of talk in this field that it was
impossible to disentangle voices and relate sounds to any meaning. Further experiments are needed here. But on one point
the scientist was rewarded. The microphones and amplifiers
picked up something which no human being had heard before,
a soft murmur among the crows, probably their love-talk.

Jackdaw Love-story

The love-making of jackdaws has been observed by Professor
Konrad Lorenz. It is very romantic.

He describes how the chief bird in a flock set his heart on a beautiful jackdaw maiden. He sat confidently in their future nest and called her with a high, sharp 'zick, zick, zick'. Among all the females present how was she to tell that this was meant for her? By the language of the eyes, the fact that the male gazed at her with unconcealed ardour.

Meanwhile she looked about in all directions except that of the 'zicking' male. Or rather, she did look in his direction for a fraction of a second, and that told him what he wanted to know. Indeed, her silent consent drove him quite crazy. In the normal so peaceful and orderly jackdaw community he began a scuffle with the next male he met – only, of course, because he thought she had looked at him.

The jackdaw maiden indicates consent by bowing submissively, with a peculiar quivering of the wings and tail, while the male approaches in the maximum display posture, with feathers ruffled and lobes of the lung powerfully distended.

Then there begins the exchange of demonstrations of affection. They bill and coo, making sounds that seem very childish in adult animals, and they do not give up making them as long as they live. Even on meeting again after a short parting in old age, they behave as if they were still on their honeymoon.

Jackdaws live as long as human beings. As, however, they marry at the age of two, their marriages last longer than human marriages.

Important social events in a jackdaw community become common knowledge surprisingly quickly, and this was noticeably the case when the leading bird described above plighted his troth to 'a low-class girl' of whom nobody had previously taken much notice. In no time at all everybody knew all about it, and she was treated with due and proper respect even when unescorted.

She took advantage of her position by letting no opportunity slip of scoring off all her previous social superiors. If a bird dared give her a rather malicious look from a distance, she charged in at once and put it in its place. In short, so far from displaying any magnanimity, her behaviour was distinctly vulgar.

If a member of the upper classes, perhaps in ignorance of the latest developments, felt tempted to take liberties with her, when hard pressed she would utter a shrill cry of distress in a rapid staccato, a deep, full 'yup, yup, yup', which might work up into fury. Every jackdaw in the flock who heard the cry of distress would promptly fly to the spot and join in it *fortissimo*. What did the would-be seducer do then? He behaved like a thief who shouts 'Stop thief!' louder than anyone else, and joined vigorously in the chorus. The excitement gradually died down, and harmony was restored. That is how breaches of the peace are promptly and effectively dealt with by jackdaws.

Jackdaws Never Forget

If a jackdaw spots a local boy robbing a nest, it kicks up an almighty row, and this lets loose a furious attack on him by all the members of the flock in the neighbourhood. Indeed, it has been known for a pair of black bathing-trunks innocently dangling from a boy's hand to be mistaken for a slaughtered jackdaw, which has led to the boy's being persecuted for life. He is branded once and for all as Public Enemy No. 1, and is angrily croaked at whenever he appears. Not just the eye-witnesses but, after a few days, all the jackdaws in the neighbourhood vent their fury on him whenever they see him. This is taken up by the younger generation — no doubt the jackdaw mothers warn their little ones against him — and, if he does not move from the neighbourhood, years later, when he has become an old man, he will still be accompanied wherever he goes by the angry scolding of jackdaws.

While out hunting for food, an enterprising jackdaw encourages its companions to venture farther from the nesting area with a protracted 'kyah'. As an indication that it is time to be going home, it will fly over its mate as she pecks about in a field and let out an anxious 'kyoo', whereupon she takes fright and sets off home immediately.

The delicate gradations in the emotional life of animals and the fine shades of tone and gesture with which they express feelings and convey them to others of their kind is astonishing. They have developed a clear and simple language with which they communicate with their fellows, sometimes showing, as in this instance, a genuine concern for the interests of their community.

Courtship Dance

The courtship behaviour of drakes reminds one of ceremonial at a royal court. The performance takes place in the water. The male suitors gather together, and the females form a circle and look on with interest.

The drakes then perform a complicated series of ritual dance movements. The routine of the mallard drake, for instance, is as follows:

Shakes tail – rocks body up and down – shakes tail – swims with a bow – tosses up drops of water with beak, first with a whistle and then with a grunt – shakes tail – adopts display posture with wings folded high – glances at chosen female – swims with a bow – shows back of head.

This can be repeated any number of times.

Eider drakes, Turkey or Peking drakes have a different routine, omitting some items of the above, but including

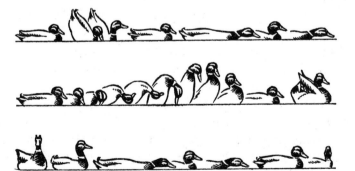

The series of dance movements in the courtship ceremonial of the mallard drake described in the text.

131

others. The females take notice only if the routine is strictly adhered to and nothing is added or omitted and no mistake made. An especially virtuoso performance by a drake may result in one female, or several, enthusiastically swimming right into the ranks of the performing males, bowing excitedly as she does so.

No matter how correctly and gracefully a mallard drake may exhibit his talents to a female teal, for instance, it makes no impression.

This discovery in duck behaviour gave Professor Lorenz an idea. He decided to find out what happened when two different breeds of duck were crossed. What was the influence of this on the courtship-dance ritual?

The drakes of the new mixed breed produced a new routine of their own, including items characteristic neither of the father's nor the mother's side. Still more curiously, the females responded to this routine only, ignoring even that of their closest relatives. Such are the strange consequences of mixed marriages among ducks.

How it comes about that a change in heredity leads to the creation of a new instinctive gesture language among the males which is instinctively understood by the females is one of the many mysteries of nature that are still not understood.

The purpose of the phenomenon is obvious enough. Failure to respond to the wooing of the wrong male results in strict segregation of duck types. Cross-breeding between different types of duck is perfectly possible biologically, but their behaviour, the so-called ethological barrier, prevents the unrestricted development of new types.

It Speaks with Its Legs

The chirp language of grasshoppers and crickets presents us with a similar phenomenon. In virtuosity it yields nothing to the language of birds.

Dr. Huber, of Tübingen University, has tape-recordings of nearly 500 different types of sound made by the grasshopper, but interpreting them is a task of immense difficulty, as these creatures have no 'mimicry'. The grasshopper, as we have known for some time, speaks with its legs, it 'fiddles' around with its toothed hindlegs on a stridulate vein on the two fore-wings, making a sound resembling that of a saw being scraped along a metal grating. Other species rub the raised forewings against each other or make a crunching noise with, the jaws which is audible at a distance.

These insects, depending on the variety, hear either with their front legs, in the upper part of which there are tiny,

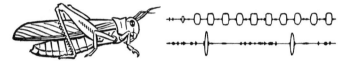

Left – A grasshopper with its 'speech' organs: the hindleg armed with teeth and the stridulator on the wing.
Right – Vibration diagrams of the songs of a male field-cricket. *Above*, the opening line of the war song; *below*, that of the courtship song.

barely visible tympanic membranes, or with similar sense organs in the abdomen.

This unusual way of hearing seemed so strange that for a long time scientists denied that grasshoppers used chirping for communicating with each other. It was held that they were brought together for mating by 'magnetism' or 'mysterious rays'.

Professor Regen demonstrated simply but conclusively that all such hypotheses were wide of the mark. To eliminate smell, or any alleged supernatural powers, as a possible means of communication, he made a male field cricket telephone to a female. The female promptly tried to creep into the receiver.

The chirpings of grasshoppers are divided into verses, lines, syllables and impulses. Each has its special meaning.

An impulse is the act of plucking at the stridulate vein by a femoral tooth. A syllable is the sound, lasting about a hundredth part of a second, caused by a femoral movement.

Notes varying in length, loudness and modulation are produced depending on how many teeth the creature rubs over the stridulate vein and the muscular force it uses. These in turn are ingeniously combined into lines and verses.

Ritual songs are exchanged in the high grass or hay between the males and females of many grasshopper species. First, the male sings his song. It means something like: 'Here am I, a grasshopper of the *Chorthippus biguttulus* species. I feel a great longing for a partner of the same species and stock.'

Eternal Triangle

If this song is picked up by another grasshopper, it will answer when a pause takes place, and, if the two songs correspond, the male takes an accurate sound-bearing while the other is chirping, and then makes a powerful leap in the direction of the invisible singer.

The latter, however, may be not a female, but another male, and a dangerous rival into the bargain. The wooer therefore takes the precaution of occasionally alternating the war-cry with his mating song.

If the other party replies with the war-cry, the case is clear. It is another male, and there is no point in pursuing the matter. The two disappointed suitors continue their search for a mate elsewhere.

But, if no war-cry comes in answer, it must be a female and, after some brief transitional chirping, their song turns into a love duet. But now and again the male emits a brief war-cry to scare away possible rivals.

If a rival is determined to get this female and refuses to be scared, the outcome may be a battle royal. When the two males come face to face, they stalk towards each other in high-stepping display posture, lash wildly in the air with their antennae and shake themselves. Between-whiles they lift their abdomen and strike out backwards with a jumping leg, to display their strength. If this is of no avail, both sound their war-cries. They open their jaws, leap at each other, strike out at each other with their forelegs, butt each other like ibexes and as a last resort try kicking with a jumping leg. If this hits its mark, it sends the victim flying from eight to twelve inches in the air.

After a knock-out blow like this, if not before, the defeated party quits the field, silently, or at any rate very subdued, leaving the victor to give voice to a fury of triumphant chirping. These fights may last for up to two minutes, but physical damage is exceedingly rare.

Language Barrier

By hard practice Dr. Loher learnt to imitate grasshopper language with his tongue, and chirped like a female in answer to a male. In every interval of his song the male took a great

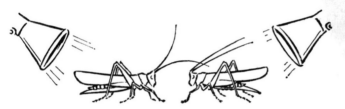

Experimental device by means of which male and female grasshoppers can be persuaded to mate.

leap towards him, hopped on to his outstretched hand, then on his forearm and upper arm, and finally into his open mouth.

Male and female grasshoppers recognise each other simply and solely by their song, and distinguish themselves from other kinds of grasshoppers in the same way. Two closely related species, *Chorthippus biguttulus* and *Chorthippus brunneus*, are physically almost indistinguishable, and their differences in song are very small. But they are sufficient to prevent all communication between them, and in their natural state mating between them is practically out of the question.

They can, however, be tricked into it by man. A *brunneus* male and a *biguttulus* female are put face to face with a small loudspeaker behind each. The characteristic song of each is played from a tape-recording from the direction of its opposite number.

Thus the *biguttulus* female hears the real *brunneus* song as well as the *biguttulus* song reproduced by the loudspeaker coming from the direction of the *brunneus* male, to whom the same situation applies, though the other way about. What happens next is most peculiar. Each insect ignores the other's real song, and is duped by that coming from the loudspeaker into believing it has met a partner of its own species. Without ever discovering the error, the two insects leap at each other and mate.

As with ducks, here are two types separated only by a language barrier which can be circumvented.

Scent Signals

Many kinds of insect use a very strange kind of language, that of scents, by which they send signals over surprisingly great distances. For this purpose they secrete hormone-like substances for which Professor Peter Karlson of Munich has suggested the names of pheromones, or perhaps more specifically telemones. The female of the silkworm moth, for instance, informs males at a great distance that she is ready for mating by exuding a definite perfume from her abdominal glands.

The male moths can scent the presence of a female from incredible distances. Human beings can scarcely perceive the finer odours a few yards away, but silkworms can detect females hundreds of yards away simply and solely by scent. To determine the distance from which the love scent is perceptible, scientists released specially marked silkworm males from a train at regular intervals. Some found their way back to the gauze cage in which the scented females were left from seven miles away — a distance over which hailing or indeed any optical signalling would have been impossible.

Yet the female possesses hardly one ten-thousandth of a milligram of this perfume, of which at any given moment only a minute proportion is exuded into the air, where it is further rarefied to an incredible extent. But these inconceivably minute traces rouse lively reactions in the male, and can cause it to trace their source from a distance of several miles.

Moreover, the few scent molecules which strike one or other of the total of 40,000 sensory nerve cells in the antenna of the male control it dictatorially throughout its brief span of life, which is truly ethereal, and begins when it slips out of its pupation. At first it hardly moves, does not fly, but remains inert, resting in some sheltered spot.

It does so with good reason, for throughout its life it lives only on air and love. It is incapable of absorbing the smallest morsel of food or drink. When the ration it took with it on leaving its chrysalis is exhausted, it dies. It must therefore husband its resources if it is to fulfil the function for which it was born. Flying about at random in the hope of finding a female would be an unpardonable squandering of its strength.

So it sits and waits patiently until the wind blows a few female scent molecules at its antenna, which looks like a palm frond. Then it has no more choice. As if drawn by invisible strings, it soars aloft and struggles against the wind until it reaches its goal or its strength fails. If a scentless female is held under its nose, however, it ignores it.

Similar scent signals are used to give the alarm on the approach of an enemy in ant or termite states, and rouse them to such a frenzy for battle that they will sometimes blindly sacrifice themselves and plunge to their ruin. Ants use another scent to mark out their routes. Bumble-bees mark their flight lanes to fields rich in blossom and nectar by leaving their 'path-finder' perfume on stalk-tips and stones.

Bees make a still more efficacious use of scent. When famine prevails in the hive and a foraging bee makes a really sensational discovery of nectar, the normal bee language (to be described in the next chapter) is not capable of quickly mobilising a sufficiently big labour force, so the bee reports its discovery by turning out a scent-pocket in its abdomen and flies off again, leaving behind a kind of vapour trail of odour, which myriads of its fellows then follow to the source of the nectar.

State-forming insects such as ants, termites and bees are informed by scent 'bulletins' whether their king and queen are thriving or not, because if their state of health gives rise for anxiety the rearing of replacements must be put in hand at once.

Twenty Years — Six Milligrammes

Professor Adolf Butenandt, the Nobel prizewinner and president of the Max Planck Society, had long been attracted by the idea of artificially imitating the scent-language of insects. After twenty years of arduous labour, he succeeded in 1959 in isolating six milligrammes of odorous substance from the scent glands of half a million female silkworms, analysing it chemically and then producing it artificially. So effective was it that within a short time the scent-bowl containing it was surrounded by a thick cloud of males.

A surprising feature of this long-sought substance is its relatively simple chemical constitution. It is merely a doubly unsaturated alcohol of the formula $C_{16}H_{30}O$. To be effective, the geometrical arrangement of the atoms in the molecular chain must be exactly reproduced. The males ignore synthetic scent molecules of the same chemical formula but with a single atom misplaced.

This led Dr. Dietrich Schneider of the Max Planck Institute to suggest the hypothesis that in this case the smelling was not, as had been assumed, a chemical but a mechanical process — that is to say, that the sensation of smell was not the result of a chemical reaction between the odorous substance and constituents of the sensory nerve cell in the moth's antenna, but depended on the shape of the scent molecule, which is inserted into the membrane of the sensory nerve cell like an oddly shaped wedge.

For practical purposes the decoy substance of the silkworm is certainly not of very great interest. It would be far more advantageous if we had the decoy scents of such creatures as the noxious cotton-spinners, vine moths, fruit moths, nun moths and other pests, so that they could be used in infested areas for luring the males into traps. If the females are left without males, they lay only infertile eggs from which no caterpillars can develop. At Professor Butenandt's suggestion, research is taking place with a view to developing this technique. It would be a hopeless task to repeat for every single species of moth the procedure used in the case of the silkworm, that is to say squeezing out half a million female scent glands to obtain a few milligrammes of the required substance.

The problem is therefore being tackled from a different angle. Different chemicals are exposed to see whether they act as decoys to the males of any particular insect species. Experiments are in full swing, and the first success has already been scored. Dr. M. Jacobsen had succeeded in producing synthetically the decoy substance of the gypsy moth, the caterpillars of which are a pest to fruit and forest trees.

This method of pest control would have many advantages. It is non-poisonous, has no effect on any other species, and is dangerous only to the insect it is desired to control. The species concerned cannot develop immunity to it, as it does to D.D.T. or other insecticides, and the balance of nature is not disturbed; it merely prevents an abnormal increase of a pest without exterminating the species.

No doubt before long it will be possible to produce commercially the odorous substance with which bees perfume their nectar air bridges. Dr. Max Renner, of the Zoological Institute of Munich University, has shown that this is the same for all bees (in contrast to the hive odour, which is dependent on the combined scent of the blossoms visited by the bees of that hive – it is by this that the bee door-keepers recognise 'outsiders'). Fruit-growers would then have at their disposal the long-desired magic substance that would ensure pollination, for a small dish of the stuff would ensure that bees from far and wide visited the orchard.

11

THE LANGUAGE OF THE HIVE

Directional Dance

THAT 'parliamentary debates' take place in the bee state is not a modern fairy-tale, but one of the most extraordinary scientific discoveries of recent years.

When the fate of the swarm is at stake, or the question arises of finding a new home for a swarm, discussions take place which begin with lively clashes of opinion. 'Experience' ranging over hundreds and thousands of years has taught these creatures that they can survive only if they achieve agreement on an objective basis.

Bee debates naturally presuppose the existence of a bee language. Just as Champollion deciphered Egyptian hieroglyphics and Grotefend the Persian cuneiform characters, so has Professor Karl von Frisch, the Munich zoologist, made his life-work the unravelling of the secret of the language of bees.

One sunny spring day his two daughters hid a dish of honey in their big garden and challenged their father to find it.

He opened his bee-box, looked into it for about two minutes, and said: 'North-north-west, 340 yards away.' He stepped out the distance and found a bush, the buzzing of the bees in which revealed the presence of the hidden honey.

How did he find it so quickly? It had been discovered by foraging bees, who were busy telling their hive-mates about it. He simply 'listened in' to their conversation.

When a bee has discovered a field of flowers with plenty of nectar, it returns to the hive and, after delivering its load of nectar or pollen, makes an announcement to the following effect: 'Attention, please. A few [or many, or a great many] workers are needed on the buckwheat in bloom in such-and-such a direction and at such-and-such a distance.'

A simple series of movements and scents, accompanied by tail-wagging, buzzing notes and neat dance figures, enable it to communicate its meaning as precisely as others do by sound language.

Sun Compass

Here are some details of the bee code:

Attention, please. I have just discovered a field of flowers, where there is nectar in such large quantities that many of you must fly there immediately.

The returning bee is excited and to attract attention in the crush jostles rather roughly against the honeycombs of its fellow-workers. The more agitated its gestures, the sweeter, richer and nearer is the new nectar-gathering place and the greater the number of workers required there.

It is buckwheat. No need to try any other blossoms.

A complicated idea, but the bees have a simple and practical way of communicating it – by the flower scent clinging to their body.

The field is exactly west-south-west of the hive.

The bee, after the introductory nudges and scattering of scent, performs a dance. Waggling its abdomen, it takes a few steps in a straight line in one particular direction, turns sharp right, stops waggling, returns to its starting-point, advances with a waggle in the same direction again, turns left, and repeats this for about two minutes.

141

If the feeding-place indicated lies in the direction of the sun, the homing bee performs its straight tail-wagging dance up the vertical honeycomb walls from bottom to top. If it does it the other way about, it is an indication that its fellow-workers will find the field if they fly with the sun behind them. Any other angle to the sun, whether acute or obtuse, can be indicated by the bee's dancing at a corresponding angle on the honeycomb walls.

As it is pitch dark in the hive, the bees the scout has jostled follow it in antenna contact or as close as possible behind. They

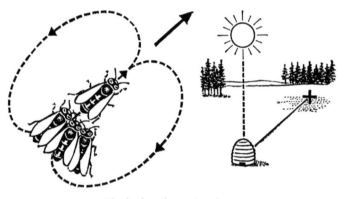

The bee's tail-wagging dance.

repeat the dance figure from one to twenty times with it and then fly straight to the place designated. Thus an 'air lift' is opened between the hive and the new source of nectar, a phenomenon which has an earthbound parallel in the routes of ants. Bees can readily be observed using these air channels.

Thus in the open air the sun is the bees' compass. In the darkness of the hive they substitute a symbol for it, the force of gravity – an astonishing intellectual achievement for the little creature.

Bees can find their way even if the sun is hidden behind clouds. At the end of the fifties Karl von Frisch demonstrated that even the smallest gap in the clouds enables the bees to tell exactly where the sun is from the direction of the rays passing through it. This feat is also performed by certain crabs, spiders, beetles and ants, but is beyond the natural capacities of man.

To perform it we need a technical aid, a so-called polarisation filter. If we look at a patch of blue sky through an Iceland spar disc and revolve it slowly on its axis, there comes a point at which the blue of the sky suddenly turns much darker; on passing it the blue is at once restored to its normal brightness. We have filtered out the light waves that vibrate only in one plane and have thus determined the vibratory direction of the light of the sky. From this the direction of the sun can be inferred even if it is obscured by cumulus clouds. This complicated equipment has been built by nature into the faceted eyes of bees.

Cloud Cover Ignored

Even when the sky is completely overcast, the bee's dances show that it is as well informed as ever about the position of the sun. How is this possible? Karl von Frisch experimented with light filters several years ago, and concluded that bees must be sensitive to the ultra-violet radiation of the sun through clouds. But this was pooh-poohed by the physicists, who said that photographic tests had shown incontrovertibly that ultra-violet light was almost completely absorbed by the cloud cover. The remainder was so widely dispersed that the position of the sun was completely obscured.

Thus the capacity for orientation and the dance language of bees in conditions of cloud cover remained an unsolved puzzle until new photographic plates sensitive to contrast came on the market in 1959. On an overcast day a telescope was directed to where the sun must be, exposures were made, and for the first time the position of the sun was recorded by ultra-violet light. Thus a splendid, though belated, physical confirmation was obtained of a piece of knowledge revealed to the biologist by bees. If the cloud cover is so thick that no ultra-violet radiation can penetrate it, the bees are at a loss and take an enforced holiday.

At regular intervals in the tropics bees are faced with a ticklish problem. On two days in the year the sun is directly overhead at noon. Consequently with the best will in the world it is impossible to say which point of the compass leads away from the sun. Bearings to right or left of the sun are

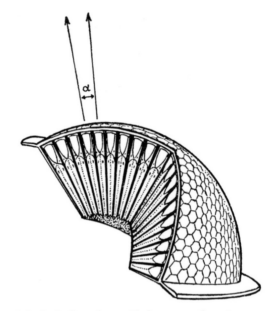

Section of the bee's faceted eye. Each separate facet is set at an angle of two to three degrees towards the next. Thus the insect can take accurate angle measurements.

equally useless. This leaves even the bees at a loss what to do. In the circumstances they do the wisest thing. They stay at home.

A few minutes later, however, when the sun has moved only two or three degrees, they can again steer an accurate course with the navigation aid of their 5,000 fixed, faceted eyes.

The explanation of this fantastic feat of precision is that two or three degrees is the angle at which two contiguous facets of the bee's eye are inclined towards each other. It is possible that the creature by means of its perception of gravity or equilibrium 'knows' which facet is pointed exactly in the perpendicular. If the sunlight strikes this, the bee brain has the 'interval signal' it requires. If the light comes through one of the six adjacent facets, determination of its course is possible again.

That brings us to the 'mathematical' processes that take place automatically in the bee's nervous system. To test the bee's mathematical faculties, Karl von Frisch and some students set up a hive in the Alps and an artificial feeding place with quantities of honey on the other side of a mountain which was too high to fly over. The bees were thus forced to take a circuitous route. How would they communicate such a complicated course to their fellows in the hive?

Needless to say, they solved the problem. The scout bees indicated by their tail dance the exact direction of the honey-store, which was straight through the middle of the mountain. The bees from the hive flew in the direction indicated until the mountain blocked their path, after which they took the nearest detour to their goal.

The ability to reconstruct the aerial line from two or more different diagonal course detours is one of the most wonderful features of their lives.

In a cross-wind the bee sets its body at an angle to its direction of motion exactly like a river ferry, to make allowance for the drift. Evidently it measures the force of the wind by direction finding from landmarks below, for the stronger the wind, the greater the slant at which it flies.

It might be assumed that homing scout bees reported to their companions in the hive the tilt towards the sun adopted by their body during flight. But here, too, the bee displays its mathematical capacity, for it so accurately takes into account the angle of drift it has taken to counterbalance the force of the wind that it announces in the hive the direct aerial line to the feeding place independently of the wind.

This ability is as useful as it is amazing, for the force of the wind can change very quickly, and variable winds might easily lead them astray.

Power Consumption as a Telemeter

The scout bee informs its fellows of the distance as well as the direction of the new feeding-place from the hive. It indicates this by the speed with which it revolves in its dance.

Karl von Frisch measured the dancing speeds used to indicate distances. In fifteen seconds the bees performed the following:

11·0 figures indicating	50 metres (164 feet)
9·2 figures	100 metres
6·4 figures	300 metres
6·0 figures	500 metres
4·5 figures	1,000 metres
2·2 figures	5,000 metres
1·3 figures	10,000 metres

In other words, the nearer the source of food, the faster the dance.

Bees fly distances of the order of 10,000 metres (over six miles) only if the nectar is very rich and supplies are short nearer the hive. A long flight is dangerous, as well as strenuous and time-consuming.

The bee's time-gauge for indicating distance is graduated to hundredths of a second. Its time sense and its capacity to infer distance from time are evidently highly developed.

If there is a great throng on the honeycomb wall, the dancer does not observe time to an exact hundredth of a second, but makes an adjustment in the next round of the dance, and the other bees, who may follow the dance up to twenty times in succession, understand this perfectly well. It has been demonstrated that they accurately 'calculate' the average figure and are guided in their flight accordingly.

This phenomenal precision work in animate nature in 1961 persuaded Dr. Harold Esch, a colleague of Karl von

Frisch's, to investigate the bee dance with a view to establishing the movements and gestures by which distance was indicated.

He put into his hive artificial bees which looked and smelt exactly like living ones. They were under the experimenter's complete control, and were capable of every conceivable movement of legs, wings and abdomen. He made them perform a completely normal dance, hoping to make the living bees fly out. This painstaking experiment failed, however. The bees followed the dummy with curiosity and joined in the dance, but did not yield to its persuasions.

Thus something was missing in the robot's behaviour, but what could it be? Dr. Esch had an idea. With the aid of a minute microphone he listened in to discover whether or not the bees accompanied their dance with sounds that no human being had ever heard. Sure enough, with the microphone suspended a few millimetres over a dancer he heard a distinct buzz every now and then in the loudspeaker.

The buzz is produced by wing vibrations when the dance has been completed and the dancer sets out again on the straight route of the waggle dance, at the end of which it ceases again. Thus the bees following in a crowded mass in the dark are given a very accurate measuring-rod. They can 'clock in' with great precision to the time taken by the dancer to cover this route and 'calculate' the distance to the feeding-place accordingly.

But how do they measure distance? If they have to fly against the wind, they report a greater distance than if the air is still, and they report a shorter distance if there is a tail wind. If they have to fly uphill, they also report a greater than the true distance. Thus it seems probable that they use their expenditure of energy as a telemeter.

They cannot complete more than eleven dance figures in a quarter of a minute. If they find nectar near the hive, that is to say, within fifty yards, they cannot indicate this by the 'waggle dance', because the speed required is too great. So they use a different technique. If the feeding-place is within fourteen yards, the scout performs a round dance, first to the left, then to the right, and so on. This means 'You will find nectar if you fly round the hive within a radius of fourteen yards.' Indication of direction is unnecessary in this case.

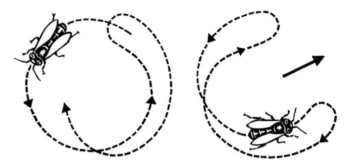

Left, the bee's round dance. *Right*, its half-moon dance.

If the food-find is at a distance of between fourteen and fifty yards, the scout dances a half-moon or crescent figure, the opening of which indicates the flight direction, as illustrated in the diagram.

Dialect Differences

Professor von Frisch conducted his experiments with German bees. There are many other kinds of bee, of course – Carniolan, Italian, Caucasian, Carthaginian, Egyptian, Indian – and there are dwarf bees and giant bees and others. Dr. Martin Lindauer, a colleague of Professor von Frisch's, investigated their language at the end of the 1950s and reached the conclusion that each type of bee has its own dialect.

German bees, for instance, indicate a distance of 100 metres by 9·2 dance figures every quarter of a minute, but Italian bees are content with 8·5 and Indian bees with 7·5 in the same length of time.

What happens if bees of different breeds are put together? Dr. Lindauer put Italian bees in a hive of German bees. He hung them in a little wire cage until they had acquired the scent of the swarm and were therefore accepted as full members.

The foreign bees were marked on the back with coloured spots to identify them. It turned out that there were considerable problems of communication. If a German bee recommended the Italians a find of nectar one hundred yards away, they flew only sixty yards, where they searched till they reached the point of exhaustion. Only then did they return empty-handed to the hive.

Expulsion of the Queen

The swarming of bees, and the debates they engage in before choosing a home, are so interesting that the whole course of events must be described in detail.

It used to be believed that the signal for swarming was given by the queen, but this is now known to be incorrect. Actually she is positively forced into leaving the hive.

For several weeks before the swarming she is fed by fewer and fewer and younger and younger workers, and sixteen days before the exodus she is given nothing more to eat, though food is available in abundance. Instead bees often jump aggressively on her back and give her a good shaking. This makes her more and more nervy. She seems to suspect that she is going to be expelled from her realm, and that the cause of this is the young queens maturing in the queen-bee cells, who have now begun from time to time to give out a low buzzing sound. She therefore tries frantically to destroy the queen-bee cells.

She may succeed in destroying one or two of them. But after that the workers are on the alert. If a bee catches her trying to attack a queen-bee cell, it rams her so violently in the flank that she falls on her side. In a twinkling more workers hurry up and form an impenetrable barrier in front of the queen-bee cell. Sometimes they form a mob round her from which she cannot escape.

Five days before the swarming, the queen, with wings vibrating, begins to 'toot' in mounting excitement. Her cries of distress grow more and more frequent, until she ends by uttering them at the rate of one a minute. Finally a hundred-headed throng of bees bears down upon her. She resists with all her might, and tries to hide in the farthest corner of the hive. But her efforts are vain. She is carried, or rather flooded out, by the bodies of her subjects. Several thousand workers follow her, and settle on a bough or beam near the hive, where they form a thick cluster, in the middle of which the queen is held prisoner.

Internal Clock

All this will have been preceded by a curious change in from forty to seventy foraging bees. Bees only swarm when an excess of nectar is present in nature. At such times homing scouts often perform their dances solo. Their fellows no longer pay them any attention, being fully occupied in gathering nectar elsewhere.

The disregarded bees look round for other tasks. They, too, have a premonition of the imminent exodus, and go searching for a new home for the swarm.

They examine every cavity, nesting-box, rubbish bin, cardboard box, hollow tree-trunk and hole in the wall in the neighbourhood to see if it is suitable for a hive.

If a scout bee decides it has found a suitable spot, it flies home and announces it by means of the waggle-dance already described. It has to make plain that the geographical data given apply, not to a field of flowers, but a possible new home. It makes this known in two ways.

In the first place, it makes no buzzing sound, this giving its hive-mates no signal to fly out. Secondly, it dances, not just for one or two minutes, but continuously and without flagging for a period of up to twenty-one hours.

While this goes on in the dark hive, the sun outside changes position. Thus it might be assumed that after a few hours the angle to the sun of the suggested new home that the bee was announcing had become so inaccurate as to be useless.

Dr. Lindauer went into this question, and found to his surprise that a mysterious time sense, an 'internal clock', which does duty as a dance speedometer with a degree of accuracy within about a hundredth of a second, also tells the bee exactly how much time has passed since it last saw the sun on entering the hive, and through what angle the sun will have travelled in the meantime.

In its waggle-dance it continuously changes its indication of direction accordingly. It can almost be said to behave like a clock on the vertical honeycomb walls.

One of these persistent dancers was observed as it began its dance at 2 p.m. At sunset it indicated exactly the direction in which the sun was sinking below the horizon. During the night it unerringly indicated the sun's position over America, then over the Pacific and then over Asia. At 11 a.m. next day it was still accurate within two degrees.

These scouts' reports, however, are never acted on immediately by the swarm. When it leaves the hive it first of all forms the familiar cluster, and it is here that the 'parliamentary debate' takes place.

The forty to seventy scouts are by no means unanimous. They begin by offering ten or even more different nest holes, the direction and distance of which they announce on the surface of the cluster by appropriate dances. Each one of them also has an opinion about the merits of the place indicated. The more enthusiastic it is about it, the more vigorously it waggles its tail.

But it would be disastrous to succumb to the wiles of a demagogue, so other scout bees who have found nothing, or nothing suitable, fly out to form a second opinion about the various proposals made.

The new home must be neither too small nor too big. It must be watertight and sheltered from the wind, must have a pleasing odour, must be free from ants, and so on and so forth. If the returning bee forms a favourable opinion, it reports accordingly to the cluster in dance language.

Gradually more and more scout bees reach agreement, and

slowly they build up a party, which grows steadily as more and more bees approve the choice. Thus the choice of an abode is the result of lively discussion. The debate may last for many days, and it may happen that a home first favoured by a majority of scouts is not occupied at all, because a minority manages to convince the majority of the superior advantages of its own proposal.

Not until practically all the scouts have reached agreement do some members of the dissenting minority relinquish their own proposal and dance in unison with the majority, though they may not have inspected the place proposed by the latter. Finally, when complete accord has been reached and nearly all the scout bees are performing the same dance, the signal for departure is given.

The waggle-dance suddenly stops, there is a great buzzing and whirring of wings, and the scout bees zigzag in all directions at great speed. The cluster breaks up, but at first the bees buzz about irresolutely in a dense swarm.

Subtraction in their Heads?

Only the forty to seventy scout bees are so far aware of the location of the new home. Only they have joined in the dance, and only a bee that has symbolically performed the flight in the hive beforehand knows which way to fly.

The scouts therefore fly a few yards in the direction of the new home, slowly return to the rear along the outer edge of the swarm, and then dash like jet fighters at speed through the middle of the swarm in the direction of the destination, turn back again, and go on repeating this performance until all the bees have arrived.

Dr. Lindauer observed a swarm in the middle of Munich, in the courtyard of the University Zoological Institute in the Luisenstrasse, which had decided on a nesting-place 800 yards away in a south-south-west direction. After flying 300 yards towards it, the swarm was broken up by a large number of cars in the station square.

The cluster quickly re-formed on the nearest traffic sign. Now came the surprise. When Dr. Lindauer caught up with them, the scouts on the cluster were indicating the direction as before, but a distance of 500 yards. Whether scouts had again flown to the destination and remeasured the distance, or had done the subtraction 'in their heads' is a question which can be settled only by further experiment. Dr. Lindauer carried out one more experiment. He set up a hive from which the bees would shortly be swarming in the middle of a plain which offered no natural nesting-place for bees for miles around. Five hundred yards to the north and 500 yards to the south he set up two identical empty hives. This created a situation of a type which can be fatal to bees.

As was to be expected, in a short time two parties of almost equal strength formed among the scout bees, and they failed to reach agreement even after dance debates that lasted for a fortnight. In the end the swarm took wing and, urged on by the two different groups of scouts, made preparations to divide. But that was out of the question, for it would leave one half without a queen. So a stubborn tug-of-war went on in the air for half an hour, and ended in the swarm's going back to the old place and forming a cluster again.

The debate then began all over again. But one party ended by giving in, and thus the problem was solved.

But sometimes bees fail to reach agreement — instances of this have been observed by Dr. Lindauer. In that case the swarm has no choice but to set up honeycombs and brood nests at the spot where the cluster has formed, that is to say in the open air. That leads to the destruction of the whole swarm by next winter at the latest.

How it Began

Dr. Lindauer's latest researches have been devoted to the question of how the bee language came into existence during the course of millions of years. Fortunately for science, there are bee species in the tropics, America and India that are at a lower stage of development. These may yield clues to the way in which bees communicated in remote antiquity and gradually developed a 'language'.

Melipolini bees, for instance, have no way of indicating distance and direction. In the case of a rich find, they urge their hive-companions to fly out by jostling against them and perfuming them with the scent of the blossoms they have found. This may have been how bee language first began. The *Scaptotrigona* bee marks out a scent path between its hive and the feeding-place at intervals of three yards on tips of grass-blades and stones, and escorts others to the destination by this route.

If the route lies over water – a pond or small lake – the scout, unlike our honey-bee, is unable to bring up reinforcements to the collecting-place. When Dr. Lindauer stretched a rope with branches spliced into it across a lake, the pathfinder bee at once marked it with its scent and brought up helpers in large numbers. They followed close behind it, in close convoy, and if a solitary bee lagged behind, the pathfinder at once went back to its assistance.

Indian dwarf honey-bees have no need of 'scent direction-finder stations' or to fly in 'convoy'. Their honeycombs are in the open, on the branches of trees, and on top of them they build a horizontal platform from which they take off. Foraging bees who have made a find alight here, and indicate the precise direction in which their companions must take off in order to find it by running in that direction themselves, waggling excitedly as they do so. They have not learnt to determine the flight direction from the angle of the sun.

The honeycomb of the Indian giant honey bee is also built in a tree-top, measures up to a yard in diameter and can weigh more than thirty pounds, but the dance-floor on the upper edge of the comb is too small for it. It has therefore 'learnt' to dance on the vertical honeycomb walls. It 'translates' the inclination of the line of flight to the position of the sun into a waggle-dance at a corresponding angle to the perpendicular. But if a board is held over the honeycomb, obscuring the sun and the sky, the dancer loses its bearings. Without being able to check the position of the sun, its language is reduced to unintelligibility.

It was *Apis mellifica*, our honey-bee, that in remote antiquity and by way of mutations of its hereditary characteristics developed its extraordinary memory for direction, distance and time, and became the most brilliant language virtuoso yet known to us in the animal kingdom.

12

INTERNAL CLOCKS OF ANIMALS AND PLANTS

When it is Time to Get Up

IT tends to be an upsetting experience for modern man if his alarm clock is out of order and he has to get up at five o'clock next morning for an important engagement. Either he oversleeps, or lies awake for hours to make sure of not doing so.

There are people, however, who can wake up more or less when they want to. Some can do so with a margin of error of a quarter of an hour, others are punctual to within five minutes. Of course special concentration just before bedtime is required to set the internal alarm clock in man.

Those that have this faculty use different methods. One man will hold his big toe as soon as he gets into bed, concentrate hard, and say to himself: 'I will wake up at five o'clock precisely.' Others do such things as kicking the springs under the mattress five times running or punching the bed-post five times. In any case, they drop off to sleep in perfect confidence that they will wake at the right time.

A mysterious time-sense operates in these people while they are asleep. Their intelligence and senses are switched off, but the internal. clock in their organism keeps on working and punctually awakens them.

In the animal and vegetable kingdoms there are internal clocks which far surpass in precision the subconscious time sense of man. How do migratory birds know the date when they must set out on their journey to distant continents? Solely and simply from their internal calendar. They postpone their start for a few days only if weather conditions are so unfavourable that they cannot fly or are likely to lose their bearings. The date of their arrival at their destination of course depends on the weather they encounter. They are often held up for several days en route.

How do the many plants whose flowers open before dawn know that the sun is going to rise in about an hour's time? By means of their internal clock. Professor Erwin Bünning of Tübingen University has demonstrated that it is not caused either by the sunrise itself or by a rise in temperature, as was for a long time supposed. He put a lot of flowers in a pitch-dark room in which a constant temperature was maintained for several days. The calyces opened every morning exactly when they would have done in natural conditions.

Plants can actually be trained to 'do things' at a definite time of day. If, say, a short sharp current of ice-cold air is blown at a plant precisely at 11.20 a.m. on several days in succession, each time it will shrink under the icy breath and its leaves will droop. After a while it will recover and its leaves will rise again.

If one morning the cold shock is omitted, the leaves will nevertheless droop punctually at 11.20 as before. Not for several days, until the plant begins to 'forget' the experience, will the reaction to the now imaginary cold shock begin gradually to fade away. Travellers on the tropical rivers in the virgin forests of Brazil are attacked in the evening by swarms of mosquitoes. The attacks take place in successive waves. As Alexander von Humboldt observed, each species forms an army of its own. When the blood-sucking period of one species is over, it quits the field and leaves it to the next. This is one of the most striking instances of different groups of living creatures having apparently come to 'temporal agreements'.

The males and females of brooding birds relieve each other at the nest in accordance with a strict time-table. In such a vital matter as care of the brood, no chances can be taken with the weather and the danger of prowling animals. The well-known German ornithologist Oskar Heinroth discovered years ago that the change of shift among these birds takes place at regular hours.

The female pigeon always sits overnight, is relieved by the male at about 11 a.m., and takes her place on the eggs again at about 4.30 p.m. If her relief is behind time now and again, she does not show the slightest impatience or annoyance when he turns up. On the contrary, he often has to use gentle force to push his way into the nest.

Touching scenes take place among the cormorants in the Galapagos Islands in the Pacific, who have no power of flight. According to Dr. Irenäus Eibl-Eibesfeldt, of the Max Planck Institute for Physiology of Behaviour at Seewiesen, near Munich, the male relief never turns up without a little present for his mate, such as a tasty starfish or a 'bouquet' of seaweed.

Love-life of the Fiddler Crab

The day of the fiddler crab is also regulated strictly by the clock. In tropical or sub-tropical coastal waters, when the silt emerges from the water at ebb-tide these little creatures crawl out of their holes in thousands, and a curious ceremonial takes place on the stretches of silt and sand glimmering in the heat.

According to Dr. R. Altevogt, of Münster University, it begins with the sorting of the freshly deposited silt into its edible and non-edible components. The females with their two eating claws shovel the silt, which is permeated with organic sediment, to their outer chewing apparatus, where a rinsing process takes place similar to that used by man in mining operations to separate ores of little value from the host rock. The organic residues of dirt and decomposition float up and are eaten, while the mass of indigestible material is formed into silt-balls and thrown away.

The males have a harder time. They have to shovel with a single eating claw, for the other has developed into an enormous fighting and signalling claw, which gives the animal a bellicose appearance but cannot be used for eating.

Ninety minutes after the tide has run out, in the midst of their busy feeding operations they are suddenly overcome with a state of nervous excitement. Practically every two seconds

A male fiddler crab has raised its huge claw to attract a female.

they raise their imposing snow-white claw to attract a female. To impress the fair sex, after the mud meal, they polish this claw with their little eating claw until it shines.

When there is a great surplus of males, the females are choosy. The males have to exhaust themselves, raising their claw incessantly for days on end before they manage to arouse enough interest in a female to cause her to interrupt her walk among hundreds of appealing males and watch any one of them brandishing his claw for a few seconds.

If a male is disregarded for several weeks, he carries out a dance in addition to his agitated call-sign. He keeps time, turns this way and that, and with his long, thin legs he performs definite figures, which vary with each of the many sub-species. The nearer a female approaches, the more furious his call-sign becomes. If he is 'accepted', he drops the female a low curtsey, drums on the ground with his giant claw and vanishes into his hole, which is up to a yard deep, hoping she will follow him with similar alacrity.

But often she just peeps cursorily into the hole and crawls on, taking no more notice of the disappointed male, who now comes darting out of the hole and signals to her disappearing form in a manner pitiful to behold. His rivals at once form an eager cordon of signallers all round her.

Every now and then there is bitter strife between two males whose holes lie about eight inches apart. When one of them thinks he has scored a success with a female and disappears into his hole, the other promptly intervenes and does everything in his power to divert her into his own desirable residence.

Just when she is about to follow him into it, however, the first male pops out again and diverts her. Things may go on like this ten or twenty times in succession until one of the two males pauses for breath in his hole rather longer than usual and his rival gets away with it.

Suddenly, however, the signalling ceases all over the vast shallows. Each crab quickly eats a little more and makes haste to repair any damage to his hole. Homeless males try quickly to dig themselves an emergency abode or to drive another out of his nest. A short and violent pushing and levering with the big claw decides the issue.

But the simplest thing for a homeless male to do is to forget his courtesy to the fair sex and simply eject a female from her hole. In an emergency a female will unhesitatingly enter the nearest male hole, where she is granted asylum without further ado. In these circumstances the male never takes advantage of the situation. Mating without the preliminary ceremonial is unthinkable.

When the final preparations and scufflings are over, the crabs all suddenly vanish into their holes and plug the entrance with mud. A few minutes later the first wave of the rising tide sweeps over the area. The crabs cannot see or hear its approach. But their internal clock, which in their case is based on the rhythm of the tides and is not on a twenty-four-hour basis, depending on the change from night to day,

others more loving than baboons are hard to find in the animal kingdom. The males in a troop of baboons also treat their offspring with much understanding.

Cock-fight conducted strictly in accordance with the rules.

tells them within five minutes when it is time to make for safety.

Even when kept in a terrarium, where there are no tides, the calling crab still lives according to the daily changes of low and high tide, an impressive demonstration of the closeness of its link with the rhythm of nature.

Honey-Bees' Duty Schedule

Most blossoms do not offer bees their nectar all day long, but only at definite times. As a rule the sweet fluid is available for only two or three hours, either in the forenoon or at midday or in the afternoon, according to species. At other times there is no nectar in their calyces, or so little as to be negligible.

Thus it would be a great waste of energy and useless exposure to all the dangers lying in wait for them if bees spent the whole day looking for nectar in a field of buckwheat, for instance, where it is available for perhaps only two hours. Hence they have an 'internal diary' in which up to five different nectar-gathering times in the day are noted.

They know perfectly well, for instance, that between 7.30 a.m. and 11 a.m. they will find plenty of nectar at a distance of 370 yards to the north-north-west, and that between 1 p.m. and 3 p.m. they will find it at another spot, and so on and so forth. In between times they doze lazily in a quiet spot on the edge of the honeycomb. But, when the next gathering-time draws near, they are jolted awake as if by an alarm clock. An inner restlessness impels them to fly at once to the right spot, where the first bees will have arrived shortly before the nectar is ready.

Karl von Frisch and his colleague Dr. Max Renner tested bees' capacity in this matter by placing glass dishes of honey at various spots at definite times every day and keeping a record of the visiting times of bees marked with coloured spots.

There is an experiment that any interested person can carry out for himself, though with rather less scientific accuracy. Anyone who breakfasts on an open terrace every morning at the same time in summer is at first bothered only by wasps. Wasps, unlike bees, have an excellent sense of smell and are attracted from a long way off by honey or jam.

But no sooner has a bee discovered the breakfast table than it alerts its hive-mates, who soon appear in great numbers. After a few days they know when it is breakfast time and appear regularly shortly before the table is laid. Apart from breakfast time, however – except very occasionally – only wasps, but no bees, will put in an appearance.

This discovery caused something of a stir even in specialist circles, because it meant that the picture of the bee as an example of untiring industry had to some extent to be revised. Outside its regular working periods it lazes in the hive. If it feels under-employed, of course, perhaps because the flowers at a collecting-place included in its time-table have faded, it seeks out the dance-floor and asks to be shown a new scene of operations to fill in the time.

Rhythm of Nature

Bees also use their internal clock for their system of communicating distance to each other and for flying by the sun compass. On longer flights, on which they take their bearings from the sun, they would not be able to find their way back to the hive if their angle of flight in relation to it were not changed to allow for its passage across the sky.

Many other creatures apparently navigate with the aid of the internal clock and the sun compass – homing pigeons, migrant birds that travel by day, crabs, fish in the ocean, spiders, ants and countless other insects. We shall return to this in the next chapter. However they perform this feat in detail, they depend in every case on the accuracy of an internal clock.

Interesting examples of this mysterious time sense occur as low down in the scale of nature as primitive unicellular organisms such as the tropical algae that produce marine phosphorescence. These minute creatures 'know' even in a darkened laboratory exactly what time of day it is, and radiate

162

a very much larger amount of light at night. More than 400 generations were reared in permanent darkness, so that they never experienced the fact of night and day. But they went on just the same – twelve hours of gleaming brightness, followed by twelve hours of feeble glow.

Like the time clock in a factory, the internal clock sees to it that the 'labour force' in every living creature is available when the whole organism requires it. The vital energy of the owl, for instance, must be fully mobilised at night, when mice and other favourite prey are abroad. Mice are stimulated to their greatest activity when they are relatively safe from dangerous enemies and conditions are therefore most favourable for getting food.

This stimulation of vital energy persists unaltered even when animals are put in an environment in which it no longer serves any purpose. At certain times of the day the tiger in its cage at the zoo prowls restlessly to and fro, though this does nothing to bring its next meal-time any nearer. This behaviour is not a result of captivity, as many people suppose. It is dictated by the great regulator, the internal clock, by which the individual creature is adapted to the cycle of life, the rhythm of nature.

Man's Forty Clocks

Man is no exception to this. So far no fewer than forty different internal clocks have been discovered in his organism. One of them regulates his body temperature, for instance, which is highest in the late afternoon and lowest in the early morning. Thus a clinical thermometer could, so to speak, be used as a clock. Unless distorted by illness, 97·7 degrees Fahrenheit (36·4 degrees Centigrade) would indicate 7 a.m. or 11.30 p.m., and 98·06 degrees Fahrenheit (36·7 degrees Centigrade) 9.20 a.m. or 8.45 p.m.

The pulse rate, blood pressure, absorption of oxygen, intestinal activity and thirty-five other reactions in the body could also be used as clocks. The only one of these of which man is consciously aware is that which physiologists call the fatigue curve, which can easily be influenced upwards or downwards by coffee or sleeping tablets. One or more of these internal processes might very well penetrate to the subconscious and give a signal to our consciousness at about the time when we should like to wake in the morning.

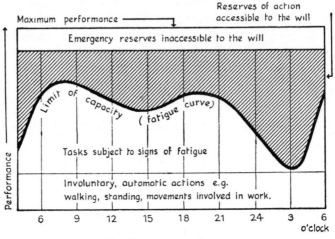

The fatigue curve of man.

Regulating the Mechanism

How accurately do the internal clocks of animals and plants keep time if they are removed from the natural rhythm of nature? To investigate this, Professor Jürgen Aschoff, head of a department of the Max Planck Institute for Physiology of Behaviour at Seewiesen, near Munich, confined greenfinches, bullfinches, chickens, mice and other rodents in a windowless room for several weeks and under continuous and steady lighting. Similar experiments can also be made with monkeys, bees, flowers, algae, with all living creatures in fact. The results are always similar.

After some time the internal clock begins to gain or lose. It runs at rates such as twenty-five or twenty-three hours a day or, say, twenty-three hours and fifty-two minutes. Gradually the internal clock of each individual slips into its own rhythm.

164

For accurate time-keeping it has to be regulated afresh by a time-signal from the outside environment. In the great majority of cases, this is provided by the sun in the alternation of day and night.

In the case of plants the sunlight penetrates into the chlorophyll where, in a way that is not yet understood, it adjusts the 'factory clock' which controls the timing of the vital processes in all the cells from the tip to the deepest root – the circulation of the sap, the production of living from dead matter, the daily cycle of the raising and drooping of the leaves and the opening and closing of the flowers, the secretion of nectar, and so on and so forth.

In most animals the time-signal is provided by the action of sunlight on the brain through the eye. The process might be described technically as a kind of frequency control, synchronising with their environment all the rhythmical processes in the sympathetic nervous system.

If vertebrates, mice for instance, are blindfolded, the regulating mechanism ceases to work. As in a room with constant lighting or kept permanently dark, the internal clock slips into its own jog-trot. With insects it is different. If a cockroach, for instance, is blindfolded, the adjustment mechanism remains unaffected. With these creatures sunlight is effective in spite of the chitinous armour of the head and directly affects places in the brain which are sensitive to light, and thus the clock continues to be regulated.

With young ants, which have been hatched in the dark depths of their nest and have never seen the sun, the internal clock is still completely unreliable. It may be as much as twelve hours fast or slow. The same applies to adult ants if they never see daylight in winter.

Clocks that are as wrong as that cannot be regulated quickly. In these cases ants can be observed crawling out of their nest and stopping still outside it for as long as three hours, watching the course of the sun, setting their internal clock by it and 'calibrating' their sun compass.

Nature has arranged things so subtlely that the weakest light capable of affecting the internal clocks of animals and plants is a little brighter than the light of the full moon. If it were darker, on moonlit nights the clocks of life would be thrown out of gear.

There are some animals, however, that set their clocks by the moon instead of the sun. One of these is a marine worm that lives in the South Seas and arranges its time-table so as to lay its eggs on the night of the new moon – a highly practical arrangement that makes both the worm and its eggs safer from predators.

The fiddler crab receives three different time-signals: the noise of the tide rushing over its closed mud-hole, sunlight and moonlight. These enable it to 'calculate its tide-tables' and know in advance when there is going to be a spring tide and consequently its territory will be clear of sea-water only for very short periods. This situation occurs at intervals of about a fortnight, and the crab arranges its life accordingly and is never surprised by the rising tide.

The time-signals that affect the internal clocks of man are much more numerous. That explains the failure of all the attempts made so far to establish the individual rhythm of man's internal clocks by shutting him up for days in a room in permanent darkness or constant light. Such things as a glance at a wrist-watch, the slightest noises penetrating from outside, moods, feelings and fantasies, all sorts of things which cannot be experimentally controlled, all play their part, and the final result is a hopeless confusion of all the internal clocks in the human organism. Everything – digestion, appetite, need for sleep, mental activity – is thrown into disorder.

A slight foretaste of these disturbances is experienced by the traveller by air to America or Japan. On arrival in the strange continent our internal clocks are as wrong as our wrist-watches. The traveller suffers from 'night shift complexes' such as constant fatigue, diminished efficiency, digestive disturbances.

After two or three days, however, everything is automatically readjusted.

Continual infringements of the natural rhythm of life, however, act like hammer-blows on a sensitive mechanism. Tomato plants, for instance, have been subjected to an unnatural rhythm with the aid of artificial lighting (seven hours of light, seven hours of darkness and so on). This resulted in disturbances of growth and malformations. The notorious alternating shift (twelve hours' day work, a twenty-four hour break, twelve hours' night work and so on) has a similar effect on man; the forty internal clocks fall into wild confusion. The stomach clock gets out of time with the liver clock. This results in stomach ulcers, heart complaints, internal pains. When man engages in space flights lasting longer than just a few days or weeks, the medical profession will be confronted with a pretty problem.

Changing the Time

To test the possibility of putting internal clocks forward or back, Dr. Max Renner put a number of bees in a refrigerator. Doing this to insects slows down the pace of the vital processes in all the body cells, the metabolism. It was assumed that the internal clock was dependent on the speed maintained by the vital processes and would become progressively slower as the temperature fell.

Strange to say, the bee clock turned out to be largely independent of temperature and the speed of cell activity. When the bees had been cooled to four degrees above freezing-point, a temperature at which they have long ceased to do any work in the hive, the clock stopped dead. It is very useful to the bees that their clocks keep uniform time whether the temperature is 60 or 85 degrees Fahrenheit (16 or 28 degrees Centigrade). But the result of the experiment makes the whole phenomenon still more mysterious.

When Dr. Renner set the internal clocks of his bees in motion again five hours later by warming them, they reached the next collecting-place noted in their diary four or five hours late, and of course returned home empty-handed. Moreover, they looked for the spot in a completely wrong direction because, when roused from their slumbers, they navigated according to a position of the sun which would have led them to it five hours previously, but now misdirected them by an angle of 45 degrees.

There is another way of altering the internal clocks of animals. They can be exposed to an artificial alternation of light and darkness, and the artificial day can be gradually and imperceptibly varied from the real day. This process takes many days and must be carried out with great care, so that the animals' internal clocks, though changed by several hours, are not put out of gear. If a time-shift of six hours is brought about in this way and the animals are then let out of the laboratory, say, at 3 p.m., they behave as if it were 9 a.m. A number of interesting experiments, which will be described in the next chapter, can be based on this.

Where is the Clock?

But where is the internal clock? Professor Bünning has systematically searched for it, both in plants and animals. Among other things, he kept sections of the intestine of the golden hamster living in an artificial culture, and noted that these small shreds of tissue retained the twenty-four-hour rhythm of their activity in the organism. Leaf joints which he cut from a plant and bisected continued to show under the microscope the same movements by which they caused the leaf to rise and droop morning and evening.

Dr. Harker suggested that the seat of the internal clock in the cockroach was in a definite nerve ganglion under the gullet. If he removed it, the cockroach remained alive, but its internal clock had stopped. If he inserted in it a similar nerve ganglion from another beetle, the clock started again, though with the individual rhythm of the donor animal.

Convincing though this sounds, the ultimate secret of the

internal clock cannot lie in a nerve ganglion, as is shown by the fact that shreds of the intestinal wall in an artificial culture unconnected with any nervous system still maintain the daily rhythm.

So the search for the internal clock went on. Microscopes and electron microscopes were used. The internal structure of individual living cells was examined, and Professor Bünning discovered that a remarkable change takes place regularly in the cell nucleus. At about midday it is at its smallest, and at about midnight it may be up to double the size. Also the various 'chemical factories' in the cell plasma, the 'protein factories, power stations, molecule converters and matter storehouses', change in structure in the course of the day.

In which of these many cellular structures does the main clock lie? Scientists at present incline to the assumption that all the components of the cell are the 'wheels' in the mechanism of the big clock and that each individual cell can act as a clock that imposes the rhythm of nature on our bodies by very complicated routes through the enzymes, the nervous systems, the hormonal glands and the nerves again. How all these 'molecular factories' are co-ordinated in the cell to act like a clock mechanism which goes on working at the same speed even when all the 'wheels' are slowed down appears at this stage to be an insoluble puzzle.

Calendar of Animals and Plants

Apart from their 'twenty-four' clock, animals and plants have a yearly internal calendar that warns migratory birds, for instance, that the time has come to take off, and tells the trees to open their buds or shed their leaves, or mammals to don their summer garment, seek out a mate or lie down and hibernate.

In the depths of winter William Rowan, a Canadian scientist, kept on the light for a few minutes after dark on four captive crows, and on each subsequent day kept it on for five minutes longer. When the days thus artificially prolonged had reached the length they naturally reach in spring, the crows became greatly excited. The migratory instinct was asserting itself. When they were released they flew north as if under an irresistible compulsion. Neither the bitter cold, nor the snow-covered landscape, nor the fact that the following days were again of wintry shortness, had power to stop them.

Professor Bünning's explanation of the phenomenon is this. Plants and animals have a precise hereditary standard of time which day by day they compare with the actual length of the day. As soon as the length of the day in spring days exceeds this standard, the internal clock gives a signal which releases a chain of reactions in the organism, including the urge to migrate.

Thus, if the inherited time standard is twelve hours and seven minutes, in our latitudes March 20th is the starting-date for the great journey. In the autumn, when the southward migration takes place, a corresponding situation prevails.

An uncanny sense of being confronted with a supernatural power in action affects scientists who keep a number of robins separately in cages so that they can see the open sky, but can neither see nor hear each other. On the same night they are all overcome by restlessness, cannot sleep, and flutter nervously about their cage. The migration fever is upon them. So precise is their annual calendar that practically all of them set out on the same night, though there has been no communication between them either by sight or sound.

Many tropical plants never or rarely blossom in Central Europe. They are usually tended very lovingly in warm living-rooms, and the sole reason for their failure to bloom is the prolongation of the day by artificial light. Their day is never short enough for the inherited time standard to be passed.

American scientists recently established that native plants can be induced to flower later than usual by artificially prolonging their day. This enables them to be marketed at times when they would normally have finished flowering.

There is no need to illuminate them all night long. Only

brief periods are necessary, amounting in all to about one-tenth of the length of the night.

One of the things that depend on the internal calendar is the egg-laying capacity of hens. Poultry farmers have turned this to account. They can light up the hen-house so as to make it 'Easter' all the year round, and the egg-laying continues accordingly.

13

WORLD TRAVEL

Bird Compass

MOST of our songbirds set out in the autumn on a great journey which sometimes takes them as far as Central or South Africa. That has been known for ages. By ringing them their routes were established, but mystery still surrounded the problem of how they found their way, which in the case of blackcaps, for instance, takes them over the Balkans, Turkey, Israel, Egypt and then up the Nile as far as the great loop. Blackcaps and other small songsters travel only at night, and not in formations like swallows, wild geese, storks and other day migrants, but individually. Many of them are young birds, making the journey for the first time, and nobody has ever shown them the way.

Two young German zoologists, Dr. Franz Sauer and his wife, have in recent years at any rate partially solved the problem. They have shown that night migrants navigate by the stars.

Dr. Sauer elicited the blackcaps' secret by a stratagem. He had noticed that night migrants took off precisely in the right direction. That is to say, they did not take off into the wind, like an aircraft, or just in any direction and then circle a few times to get their bearings, as homing pigeons often do. They knew their exact direction of flight before the take-off.

This was a great advantage to Dr. Sauer. There was no need to track their flight over a long distance. It was sufficient to put the bird in a special cage, watch it fluttering about on a ring perch until it decided the correct position for take-off, and indicated by a whirr of wings that it would take off if it were free.

When the cage was turned slightly, the bird at once adjusted its position, first moving a little too far in the required direction and then nervously and tensely swinging back to the correct position, behaving in fact just like the magnetic needle in a compass. Warblers behave in basically the same fashion in actual migration. They continually diverge from their true course by about five degrees to right or left and then correct it.

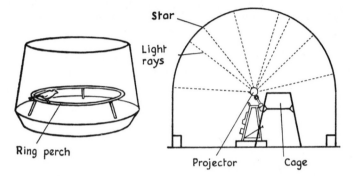

Star

Light rays

Ring perch

Projector   Cage

On the left, Dr. Sauer's special cage. The blackcap is sitting on the ring perch. It can see the stars over the upper edge. The side wall is opaque.
On the right, a cross-section through the planetarium in which the cage shown on the left was set up. In the centre is the projector, with light rays (dotted lines) falling on the dome and showing stars as small dots of light.

As the bird gave perfectly reliable information about its flight direction in its cage, there was no reason why it should not be experimented with in a planetarium.

Dr. Sauer's planetarium experiments have become famous. The idea came to him in 1956, when he noticed that if the sky was clouded, blackcaps could orient themselves for migration only if a few bright stars were visible. That provided the long-sought clue; night migrants must navigate by the stars.

The experiments were conducted in the Olbers Planetarium of the Bremen Maritime Academy, and they had their snags. Dr. Sauer and his wife took it in turns to lie on their backs under the jacked-up bird-cage in the glimmer of the dim artificial starlight of the dome-shaped hall, watching the bird, taking its bearings and noting them down. For a few days that might have been not too bad, but Dr. Sauer and his wife kept it up during the migratory season twice a year for several years.

Also, the blackcaps got very cross when they were fetched from their comfortable cages to be experimented with. Birds with which Dr. Sauer had established personal friendship had to be prevented from recognising him when he experimented with them, otherwise they grew hostile and shunned him for weeks on end. Even returning them to their homes and tempting them with freshly skinned mealworm larvae failed to restore relations to their old basis. The offended bird refused to accept these dainties from him, though it took them eagerly enough when they were offered by his wife. So he always had to put on a mask and disguise himself like a bank-robber for the experiments.

Artificial Sky

He began by showing his blackcaps at the autumn migration season an artificial starlit sky which looked exactly like the real sky over Bremen. They were completely taken in by it, and flew off without hesitation towards the south-east, i.e., in the direction of Turkey.

That of course proved nothing at all. The birds might not have been taking their bearings from the artificial stars of the planetarium, but from something quite different, such as the earth's magnetic field, perhaps, or electro-magnetic waves proceeding from space.

To meet these objections Dr. Sauer turned the projected image of the sky in all directions, but whatever he did the birds always took off towards the planetarium south-east, even if this was the real north or west, for instance.

Moreover, if in the course of the night the stars in the planetarium did not travel across the sky like the real stars, but remained stationary for several hours, the birds adjusted their direction of flight accordingly. They seemed to know that at 11 p.m. in September this or that constellation would be in the south-east, and thus in their direction of flight, but that it moved on, and by 1 a.m. for instance, would be in the south, and that at that time their course must consequently be 45 degrees to the left of it.

These experiments made it clear that blackcaps instinctively recognised individual constellations, 'knew' that they travelled across the sky during the night and also 'knew' the changes of the constellations with the changing seasons.

When their internal calendar tells them that it is mid-September, and the internal clock says that it is 11.10 p.m., for instance, they are aware of the position of the stars at that time, and consequently know where the south-east lies.

The results of these experiments are so convincing that even Professor Otto Koehler, of Freiburg, the great critic of German zoology, who refuses to accept findings that are not completely well based, agrees that these are facts that no future zoologist can ignore.

These small feathered astronomers can still navigate if only one or two stars are visible through the cloud cover. But if the sky is totally overcast, or if the whole dome of the planetarium is in darkness, they flutter helplessly about the cage for some time before deciding that there can be no finding their bearings on this occasion and dropping off to sleep. In natural conditions they simply interrupt their migration in these circumstances.

How do they acquire their extraordinary astronomical capacity? Do they learn it from their parents? To test this possibility, Dr. Sauer kept a blackcap in a closed room from the time it was hatched. It never saw another blackcap, or the sky, either by day or night.

Such animals, growing up in complete solitude and isolation from their natural environment, are known to German scientists as 'Kaspar Hauser' specimens, after the mysterious foundling of 1828, who was kept in a locked room until his sixteenth year, had not previously seen a human being, animal or plant, did not know the difference between night and day, could not speak, and did not know whether to walk upright or move on all fours. Kaspar Hauser animals are reared for the purpose of differentiating acquired and inherited modes of behaviour. In September, when this Kaspar Hauser blackcap was seized with migration fever, Dr. Sauer put it in the Bremen planetarium and switched on the stars. At first it was thoroughly startled, but then it flew off towards the south-east.

Thus the blackcap has inherited its knowledge of celestial geography and the course of the stars. Science still has no explanation to offer of how this instinctive knowledge of a subject as complicated as that of the constellations came to be embedded in an animal's germ plasm.

The mystery is aggravated by the fact that the course of the constellations changes from millennium to millennium because of the gyroscopic motion of the earth's axis. At the time of the Pharaohs the Southern Cross was visible in Europe. Birds must therefore have taken into account the changes in the night sky and absorbed them into their hereditary characteristics.

Turning-point off Cyprus

Dr. Sauer now took matters a stage further. He deluded his blackcaps into believing that they were really flying south-east. He caused new constellations to appear in the south, while familiar ones dipped beneath the northern horizon. After showing the blackcaps the night sky over Bremen, he showed them in succession that of Prague, Budapest, Sofia and western Turkey. Still they headed due south-east.

But then something remarkable happened. When he showed them the night sky of the eastern Mediterranean, as it is to be seen in the sea area round Cyprus and in Israel, the blackcap suddenly turned south, like a ship changing course. This celestial turning-point saves them going on into the Arabian desert, where they would certainly die a miserable death. Instead they are safely guided along the Nile towards their winter quarters.

It was very remarkable that on seeing the starry sky over Cyprus the bird at once turned south, irrespective of whether it had been deluded into the belief that it had flown from Bremen to Cyprus in three weeks or in the 'record time' of three hours.

The blackcap's destination is also written in the stars. If it is tricked into believing it has reached the area south of

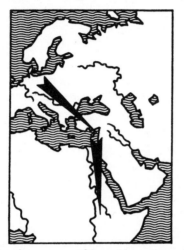

The blackcap's course to Africa, with turning-point in the Cyprus–Israel area.

the great loop of the Nile, it is content. It feels it has arrived, its nightly migration fever disappears, and it goes to sleep.

Other migratory birds are led irresistibly by the stars to other destinations. The uncanny impulse is far stronger than greed, and outweighs the attractions of a comfortable life in any of the regions through which they pass on their route, no matter how favourable the climate or abundant the food that the latter may have to offer.

The western European whitethroats and garden warblers, which migrate to South Africa by way of Gibraltar and West Africa, would find ideal living conditions on the Okawanga River in Angola, for instance. But, after taking a short rest, they abandon this fertile region and fly 160 miles across the

Kalahari desert to the Etosha Pan and into the inhospitable border areas of the Namib desert, where they have a hard struggle for survival.

The only explanation of this behaviour is that their instincts, based on the position of the stars, are more powerful than their individual wishes. Their genetic substance includes a travel ticket for the journey of life, so to speak, and they cannot escape the obligations that go with it.

The migratory instinct actually leads lemmings to destruction. In the northern regions of the Old World and the New, in years of immoderate propagation and over-population this species of vole is seized with an apparently senseless migratory impulse, which drives them in serried ranks and by the thousand into the Arctic Sea, in which they drown. Only the few animals which do not join in the death drive ensure the preservation of the species. But – paradoxical as it may sound – the death drive is vital to their survival. A possible explanation is indicated by our section on the deterioration of community life among rats.

The destination of migratory birds is presumably more or less firmly fixed by the germ plasm in their brain and nervous system. If this destination is on land, if it is accessible and conditions there are favourable, all the animals having the inborn urge to travel are able to survive.

Otherwise they inevitably perish, like the swarm of thousands of millions of grasshoppers which was sighted some time ago in mid-Atlantic, 2,000 miles away from their starting-point in Africa. If mutation causes an animal to be given the wrong ticket, it dies.

Back from Eastern Turkestan

The little blackcap is faced with a baffling problem if it is shown a spring night sky during the autumn migration period. Its internal calendar tells it that it is autumn and that it must consequently fly south-east, but the stars in the planetarium say it is spring and that it must therefore fly north-west. The result is that it flutters irresolutely between north-west and south-east.

If it is shown a summer or winter sky in spring, it does not 'recognise' the stars, as of course it never travels in summer or winter; and it flies round the planetarium with no sense of direction.

Dr. Sauer set his blackcaps even more complicated problems. During the autumn migratory season he showed one of the birds in the Bremen planetarium at 9 p.m. the night sky as it was not due to look until 2 a.m. What would it do about a sky that was five hours early? Being 'accustomed' to 9 p.m., would it fly towards the stars that would guide it correctly to the south-east at that hour, though they were now in the south-south-west? Not at all. The bird had complete confidence in the accuracy of its internal almanac and clock. If that was the position of the stars, it must mean something else. In-credible as it may sound, it decided, after a few moments of panic, that it could not be in Bremen at all, but in the place where the stars were really where they seemed to be in the dome of the planetarium, namely in eastern Turkestan.

If it were to fly south-east now, it would end up on the high plateaux of Tibet, 12,000 feet above sea-level. Instead it flew west, towards where it really belonged. Dr. Sauer thereupon presented it with the illusion that it was really flying west from Lake Balkash, just as he had previously given it that of flying to Africa, to see what it would do on each separate stage of the journey.

It flew west when shown the starlit sky over the Sea of Aral, and kept to this course over the northern part of the Caspian Sea, and the Crimean peninsula. Over the southern edge of the Carpathians in Rumania it slowly veered to west-south-west. Over the Danube east of Belgrade it changed its course to south-south-west, and over Serbia it returned to its normal south-easterly course, which would take it via Sofia to Africa.

This astonishing feat of navigation shows how the blackcap can correct its course if it is diverted by strong cross-winds.

It is a wonderful demonstration of the 'safety factor' provided by nature to protect its creatures against the disastrous effects of a disturbance of her 'time-table'.

Planets Ignored

Dr. Sauer, who is now at the University of Florida at Gainesville, Fla., is continuing his work with the golden plover. In particular he wishes to find out which of the many stars the night-migrants use to guide them.

The simplest hypotheses are that they use either the polestar or the bright ribbon of the Milky Way, but both have been disproved. It is a simple matter in a planetarium to darken an individual star or cut out the Milky Way, but doing so makes no difference to the birds.

Bright moonlight, shooting stars and summer lightning confuse them. When they were shown these natural phenomena in their special cage out of doors at night, they were startled, interrupted their south-easterly whirring and for a short time flew in the direction of the startling phenomenon.

It must of course be pointed out that that is what they did in Dr. Sauer's cage, which was so constructed that they could see only the sky, and no landmarks on the ground or on the horizon. If they are allowed ground visibility such as they have on their night flights, in the case of 'celestial disturbances' they promptly switch over to using landmarks and navigate by these for a time. On long nights of full moon they interrupt their journey.

Strangely enough, they are not in the least disconcerted by the bright planets Venus, Mars, Jupiter and Saturn. So the investigator is left with the difficult and tedious task of finding out by trial and error in the planetarium which of the constellations guide the birds over strange lands by night.

Dr. Sauer believes he has indications that the three bright stars of the Summer Triangle, Vega, Deneb and Atair, play a key part in the autumn migration period. But we must probably be prepared for surprises in this field.

Birds that migrate by night are not the only astronomers in the animal kingdom. Most moths use the stars to find their way. It has been discovered only within the past few years that moths and butterflies often need to make long, straight flights to other areas. The British professor, C. B. Williams, describes butterfly migrations in which millions and millions took part. He observed thistle butterflies broadly dispersed over a 100-mile front passing northwards over the North African coast, crossing the Mediterranean, splitting up and crowding together in the Alpine valleys, and then advancing into Central Europe in a compact column.

Cabbage Whites have been observed arriving from the Baltic area in a thick cloud like drifting snow and flying across the Channel towards England. The hawk-moth from the Mediterranean countries travels as far as Sweden and Finland, sometimes even to Iceland. Incidentally, this creature can produce peculiar sounds, resembling the squeaking of a mouse, which have struck terror into many superstitious people.

Like a migrant bird, the North American Monarch butterfly in spring and autumn traverses practically the whole of its native continent. The outward flight is usually made by one generation, and the return journey, to the place where the butterflies lived as caterpillars, by the next. At least half of all the species of moth migrate over long distances, but their journeys are extraordinarily difficult to follow.

As for butterfly methods of navigation, the only assumption so far is that they fix their course in the same way as migrant birds. The one certain fact is that moths use bright stars to keep a straight course by. If a moth sees an electric lamp instead of a star, it spirals helplessly, and may be led to its destruction. If we assume that a moth's direction of flight is set by a star at an angle of 30 degrees and at an infinite distance, its straight flight is to a great extent ensured. But, if it tries to maintain the same angle to a street-lamp quite close to it, it necessarily circles round it in a narrowing spiral until it ends by hitting the hot lamp and being burnt. Its instinctual mechanism makes no provision for behaviour in relation to terrestrial lights. That is the explanation of the apparent folly of moths in flying into the light.

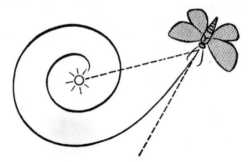

A moth, steering by maintaining an acute angle to an electric lamp, approaches it in a spiral. Should the angle be 90 degrees, it makes a complete circle round the lamp.

Scent Time-table of Salmon

There are sea creatures that, like migratory birds, make world-wide journeys in the course of the year. The sperm whale traverses all the oceans of the earth, always following the same route and the same time-table. It appears now off Hawaii, months later off Cape Town and some time afterwards off the Azores. In past centuries whaler captains knew about these sea mammals' travel routes. Herman Melville's Captain Ahab, who pursued the whale Moby Dick all over the world, is not a product of the imagination of a yarn-spinning seaman, but has a factual basis.

Tuna fish cross the whole width of the Atlantic or Pacific. Others travel yearly from the Mediterranean to Norway, and appear sporadically in the North Sea. Eels in their youthful form as small, transparent glass-eels migrate from their birth-place in the Sargasso Sea, between the Azores, the Bermudas and the West Indies, into our European rivers, and return to the Sargasso Sea for the spawning when they are fully grown.

That is only an assumption, of course, which at the moment it is impossible to prove, for how would one pick out an eel marked in our waters from a hundred thousand others at the place where it dies in mid-Atlantic?

The salmon does things the other way about. From its native place in the mountainous sources of rivers it makes it way down to the sea, and after from two to seven years, depending on the species, returns to its native mountain stream to spawn and die.

How does the salmon 'know' with such certainty in which of the numerous tributaries of the world's rivers it was born? Is the knowledge of its destination inherited from its parents, or does it take such careful note of the way on its outward journey as to be able to find it again seven years later?

As an experiment, salmon spawn was taken from a tributary of the Weser and put in one of the sources of the Rhine. Would the salmon hatched and marked there return several years later to the tributary of the Weser, the home of their ancestors, or to the place where they were born?

The result was clear and unambiguous. They returned to the spot to which they were taken by man, to the source waters of the Rhine. There was only one possible explanation; they remembered exactly the route they had followed in the opposite direction as tiny young fish.

Salmon have phenomenal memories and a phenomenal sense of smell. How highly developed the sense of smell can be in fish has been demonstrated in the case of the European eel. They are capable of discerning an odorous substance in the water if only one or two molecules of it simultaneously penetrate their nasal cavity. This means that they could detect a scent if a thimbleful of it were diluted in fifty-eight times the amount of water in Lake Constance.

That explains how salmon are able to make their way up-stream following a precise route-guide based on smell, and know whether to bear right or left whenever they come to a tributary. Sometimes they go astray, but only if the tributary smells exactly the same as the main stream. Usually they notice the mistake after swimming from six to twelve miles, and go back and take the right way.

A spawning-ground where for any reason all the salmon fry have been destroyed is never again visited by salmon. Salmon in spawning condition may be taken to such a place, or to other waters strange to them, but it is no use. An irresistible instinct forbids them to accomplish the act of propagation in strange waters, and they die without depositing the spawn. Their 'nose' ensures that their young come into the world only in the old familiar place, which experience tells them is safe.

If man changes the smell of a river, for instance by the effluent from a new industrial plant, the water does not have to be poisonous for the local salmon to become extinct. It is enough if they can no longer tell the way home by the original smell. That is one of the reasons why salmon in German rivers have decreased so rapidly in recent years.

Memory Feats

At first sight it seems inconceivable that a salmon should be able to keep in its head from early youth to old age such a vast and complicated repertoire of scents as is represented by a river and its innumerable tributaries. To the zoologist, however, this is by no means an exceptional phenomenon. He is familiar with similar examples in the animal kingdom.

Fish in coastal waters, for instance, 'learn by heart' during the incoming tide where there are deeper depressions in the sand or silt bottom, and the relative position of these. If they are later surprised by the ebb and are in danger of being left high and dry, they know at once where to find still navigable channels.

In 1960 marine biologists repeated a revealing experiment first carried out by Dr. Lester Aronson, of the Department of Animal Behaviour, American Museum of Natural History. At flood-tide they hollowed out a number of depressions in the shallows not far from the shore. As expected, fish of several species were surprised by the next ebb-tide, but by jumping from pool to pool they all managed to reach the open water very quickly. One fish actually jumped ten yards in all through eleven pools, which were laid in an irregular zigzag. Not once did it look for the next pool or the open water in the wrong direction. At the next ebb-tide a fish was kept prisoner for a short time in the highest pool while one of the pools was filled up. When it was released, it jumped on to the dry spot where a pool should have been, and would have died there if it had not been picked up and put back in the water.

American scientists have put fish in a giant aquarium with artificial tides and succeeded in getting them to remember the position of such pools for as long as forty days with no sight of them in between. Over a longer period than this, however, their memory failed.

Yet another example. A mouse can find its way back like a flash to its hole in the pantry cupboard, cellar or open country in the dark only because it has learnt every step of its territory by heart. On its first night reconnaissance of a strange area, for every three steps forward it takes about two steps back. Such is the precision with which it learns its way about that on each excursion through its territory it follows precisely its own previous footsteps, and thus moves about rather like a tram on invisible lines with fixed points and crossings.

Professor Konrad Lorenz once played a trick on a water-shrew. Across one of the beaten tracks it had memorised there lay a block of wood three inches high on to which it used to jump. One day he removed the obstacle and made it traverse the long familiar track, and in broad daylight. The result was absurd. When the creature reached the spot where the block of wood should have been, it jumped up blindly and fell flat on its belly, squeaking with terror.

Bearing all this in mind, it seems perfectly credible that the salmon should be able to note for later use an exact olfactory route-guide to its native river. How it is able to find its way to the mouth of its native river in the vast expanses of the ocean, however, is a different matter.

Professor Arthur D. Hasler, of the University of Wisconsin, has established that salmon travel from twenty-eight to thirty-five miles a day at sea, and are able to navigate in the approximate direction of the mouth of their native river from distances of 3,750 miles. It is not so easy to determine the course taken by fish in the open sea, so Professor Hasler used this stratagem. He netted some salmon from a trawler south of the Aleutians in the North Pacific and fixed a glass flask to their bodies. Every three hours this released a tablet consisting of a powder which dyed deep red the surface water over the place where the fish had just passed. This made it possible to follow the salmon's course from a helicopter for two days. The marking apparatus did not work for longer than that.

Professor Hasler has evolved a plan which he hopes will make it possible to follow the salmon's course for weeks with greater ease and without the use of a helicopter. He proposes to catch a salmon at sea and try to strap round it a 'belly band' attached to a fifty-yard-long nylon cord, the free end of which will be held above the surface by a balloon. In the gondola of the balloon there will be a small wireless transmitter by tuning in to which it will be possible to establish the fish's position at any time, and thus plot its course. The professor hopes that the fish will go on dragging the balloon behind it for weeks. The future will show whether this idea is practicable or not.

In his laboratory Professor Hasler built an aquarium which allowed cichlids and sunfish, like Dr. Sauer's blackcaps, to travel in the direction they preferred. When the sun was allowed to shine into the aquarium, the fish showed a pronounced trend in direction. When the sun was shaded off with a piece of cardboard and they were led by a mirror to believe in a false position of the sun, they promptly changed course to that which they would have followed if the sun shown by the mirror had been the real sun.

These experiments demonstrate that fish navigate at sea by the position of the sun, and thus, with the aid of their internal clock, have an excellent 'compass' at their disposal. Indeed, they must necessarily be able to make accurate allowance for the refraction of the light of the sun by the surface of the water. In the North Pacific and other sea areas also in which salmon travel the sky is often heavily overcast for weeks on end. They are obviously still able to find the mouth of their native river in spite of that. There seems to be no question of their being guided by ultra-violet or polarised light, as bees are. So there must be other things beside the sun by which salmon find their way, but these still lie beyond our ken.

That two quite different methods of orientation can be used is shown by wolf-spiders. These arthropoda, which do not make webs, but leap on their prey, frequently live on the shore of lakes and, like water-spiders, can walk about on the surface of the water to chase insects.

When danger threatens they make a bee-line for the shore and hide under stones or in grass. If the sun is shining, they simply use their sun compass and internal clock to find the way. If the mirror experiment is made with them, and they are shown a sun which has been moved 180 degrees from its true position, they dash out on to the open lake, though the shore is clearly visible.

If the sky is overcast and they cannot take their bearings from the sun, they are guided by the outline of their native shore and make straight for it. Thus their use of the sun compass appears to exclude that of the apparently more obvious means of navigation.

How did the sun compass originate? How did bees, ants, birds that migrate by day, homing pigeons, fish and many other creatures, develop the capacity for using the momentary position of the sun in conjunction with their internal clock to travel towards a required point of the compass? Dr. Marianne Geisler, of the Zoological Institute of Göttingen University, in 1961 made an interesting discovery in this connexion. Some kinds of water-flea, the *Cladocera*, can only make directly towards the sun. They cannot travel at an angle to it. Hence the path they cover in a day takes the form of a semicircle.

Another species of minute crustaceans, *Mysidium*, can travel either straight towards the sun or at right angles to it.

The black-armoured dung-beetle can also steer at an intermediate angle of 45 degrees to the sun, but has no real freedom of choice between its three possible courses in relation to it. On the contrary, it is a helpless slave of the clock, as Dr. Geisler has shown. At dawn it cannot help crawling straight towards the sun. At about 9 a.m. its instinct suddenly impels it to use its right eye to keep the sun at an angle of 45 degrees. Later on it changes course to keep the sun exactly broadside on.

At about noon it turns in its tracks to keep broadside on to the sun with its left eye, and at about 3 p.m. reduces the angle to 45 degrees, and later it again advances straight towards the setting sun. If its daily course is plotted as it would be by a pilot, the curious fact emerges that in the morning it always goes east and in the afternoon west, following almost the same track.

This suggests that in other insects finer divisions in the angle of inclination to the sun developed gradually in the course of evolution — first nil degrees, then nil and ninety, then forty-five and ninety, and so on.

With bees, ants and many other insects this development has reached finality. Changes of inclination are much less violent, and take place in small and hardly perceptible gradations of only two or three degrees, corresponding to the angle of inclination of two adjacent facets of their eyes (see drawing on page 144). Moreover, they can be freely chosen by the insect independently of the time of day.

Homing Pigeon Mystery

In bees and ants calculation of the homeward course by the sun compass is relatively simple. They merely repeat their outward course in the opposite direction, and this brings them safely home. It does not matter if they have done a lot of zigzagging on the outward journey; from the aggregate of all their angles of inclination and distances they can reconstitute the exact aerial line to their hive or nest. These facts are still dawning on us, astonishing as they are.

With homing pigeons, the problem is completely baffling. They can be taken in a pitch-dark box on a complicated journey, with all sorts of detours, 100 miles from their home, yet no sooner are they released in a totally unfamiliar place than they take off and, after from ten to twenty seconds' sight of the sun, set off in the direction of their home loft.*

It seems impossible that a carrier pigeon in a closed box on a long and circuitous car drive can be sure of its position at every moment. So Dr. G. V. T. Matthews, of Cambridge University, suspects that pigeons (like the blackcap which was persuaded by the stellar sky that it had been driven off course to eastern Turkestan) take an astronomical reading of their longitude and latitude, compare it with the longitude and latitude of their home loft, and from that compute the angle of inclination at which they must fly.

That sounds like higher mathematics. A trained ship's officer would need a sextant, a chronometer and from ten to fifteen minutes of calculation before coming up with the answer. But the instinct of the homing pigeon produces it

* Not all pigeons set off for home, but some do. The direction may also be different from that of the home loft, though the majority may set off in a specific direction rather than at random.

after it has had only twenty seconds to observe where the sun stands in the sky.

The situation may be visualised as something like this. A homing pigeon based in Hamburg 'knows' exactly where the sun should be at any given time of day. If it is taken to Bremen, for instance, it sees at once that the sun, in relation to where it would be over Hamburg, is 0·5 degree too far north

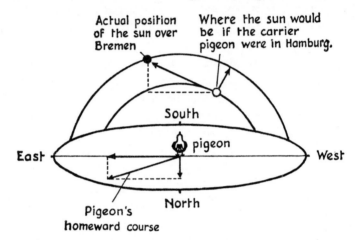

The homing pigeon calculates its homeward course thus. If in the strange place (Bremen) it looks south, it sees that the sun is farther to the north-east than it would be at home (Hamburg) at that time of day. So it must fly north-east if it wants to reach its home loft.

and 1·25 degrees too far east. Consequently it must fly north-wards and eastwards to get back to Hamburg, at the exact angle of inclination to the sun to the position in which it would be over Hamburg.

The pigeon flies in this direction until the real position of the sun agrees with the estimated position. By that time the bird is close to its home and can find its way by familiar landmarks.

To accomplish this feat it must have a protractor accurate to within fractions of a degree and an internal clock accurate to within a few seconds. Breeding homing pigeons obviously means breeding birds with an extremely accurate internal clock.

Gustav Kramer demonstrated as follows the important part

played by the internal clock in the orientation of homing pigeons.

He put birds in a darkened laboratory and exposed them with electric lighting to an artificial sequence of night and day. Slowly and gradually he caused this to depart from the natural sequence, and thus altered their internal clocks by six hours. When he then released them in a strange place, they set off in the wrong direction. They arrived home safely, but with some delay. They must have noticed the fraud on the way and re-adjusted their internal clock.

Homing pigeons' behaviour when released in thick cloud cover is completely baffling. Most of them sooner or later find their way back to their loft even without the sun compass. This phenomenon is obviously similar to that we mentioned in the case of the salmon. No one can yet explain how they perform this feat. Gustav Kramer made some curious observations in connexion with it. He started some Wilhelmshaven pigeons from Cloppenburg in thick cloud cover, and followed them for two or three minutes through field-glasses. He released them one at a time, and they flew separately. In clear weather they always made a bee-line for Wilhelmshaven, but this time they flew off in the direction of Emden. Even so, they got back to Wilhelmshaven only a little late.

Because they nearly all took practically the same course towards Emden, Dr. Kramer spoke of a 'misdirection' in their case. In the absence of the sun, these creatures must be guided home by some factor unknown to us. It does not show them the most direct course, but one that deviates slightly from it – this strange 'misdirection', in fact.

Further bad-weather experiments showed that at the same place and on the same day this 'misdirection' was always approximately the same with different pigeons. But it was different at different starting places on the same day, and on different days it differed at the same place. These 'misdirections' that vary with time and place seem so utterly inexplicable that we cannot even put forward a hypothesis to explain them.

American scientists hope to be able to shed fresh light on the problem by equipping carrier pigeons with light radio transmitters and thus following their whole course.

Cat in a Bag

Though we can throw at any rate partial light on the homing instinct of salmon and homing pigeons, we are completely in the dark about it in the case of other animals.

Professor H. Precht and Dr. Elke Lindenlaub performed the

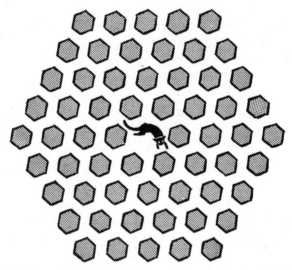

This labyrinth made of hexagonal cartons has twenty-four exits. The cats (or mice) were put out in the centre. Nearly all the animals used the exit that lay exactly in the direction of their own home.

following experiment at Wilhelmshaven in 1954. They put a cat into an opaque bag and, after taking it on a roundabout drive through the town, put it in a dark laboratory in the centre of a labyrinth with twenty-four exits leading in every direction. They waited to see which exit the cat would choose, and repeated this with 142 other cats.

An overwhelming majority emerged through the same exit, that which lay exactly in the direction of their home.

Similar results were obtained by Elke Lindenlaub with mice.

The 'palm-fronds' of the silkworm antenna contain 40,000 separate sensory nerve cells of various types. With them moths can feel, discern many odours and determine the direction of the wind. Just a few scent molecules are sufficient to impel a male to search out a female.

The grasshopper's vocabulary includes nearly 500 different chirping sounds, which it produces with the saw teeth on the hind leg.

Two bees feeding communally.

This feat is obviously utterly beyond the capacity of the human senses, and we are still completely baffled by it.

A similar secret is possessed by the limpet. It lives all its life in the same home on rocks in the tidal zone of the sea, and the lower edge of its shell fits into the corrugations of the rock surface, making it watertight. When the tide comes in, it always makes for this place, at which alone it can make itself safe, snug and watertight.

When the tide is out, it creeps for several yards over the rocks

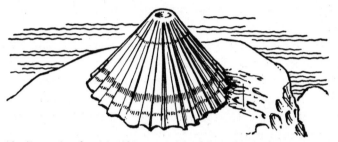

The limpet has fitted itself in watertight fashion by the lower edge of its shell into the grooving of its native rock.

to feed on algae. No matter where it roams, it always finds its way back punctually to within fractions of a millimetre of its home.

To discover what sense organ the limpet used for this, various attempts were made to prevent it from getting home before the incoming tide. Its eyes were bandaged, the contours of the rock were altered with hammer and chisel, corrosive acid was poured over the rock to remove traces of scent. In spite of all this, the creature got home punctually and unerringly every time.

Toads, like salmon at the spawning season, return to their native place every year to lay their eggs. Dr. H. Heusser observed numbers of these anurans emerging from a wood and advancing at the rate of 600 yards a day towards an area of marshland and lakes several miles away. They kept to quite definite routes, which were not the most direct, but curved to take into account the irregularities of the terrain.

The routes all went in the general direction of the spawning area and did not split up into 'private' routes to individual spawning grounds until shortly before the destination. It made no difference whether the sun was shining or the sky was heavily overcast. The creatures kept unerringly to the prescribed course.

If hot sunshine dried up their native pool after they had reached it, they never looked for another that still held water, though there were plenty of these all round. Instead they dug themselves down into the marsh and waited until enough rain fell to allow spawning to continue.

In the winter of 1956–57 a motor road was built across these spawning-grounds. Regardless of the concrete track, in March the toads made straight for the same spot, where they crawled about in desperation and were run over wholesale. There were plenty of pools only a few yards away, but these they disdained, because their instinct allowed them to spawn only in the place where they were born.

The fate of a toad population is thus irrevocably bound up with that of its native pool. If the pool silts up, its fate is sealed.

Similar mysteries can be told of many other creatures, bats, for instance, or seagulls, which in the darkened lecture hall of Kiel University tried to fly in the exact direction of their breeding-places. In all these cases they must obviously be guided by obscure sense organs, following signs that are hidden from us. They live in a world which is so strange to us that even partial success in exploring it is still denied us.

Terrestrial Magnetism or Electro-Magnetic Rays?

The young German zoologist Dr. Hans Georg Fromme, of the Zoological Institute of the University of Frankfurt-am-Main, is investigating the mysterious capacities and senses by which animals find their way. He is experimenting with European robins which, like blackcaps, migrate singly and at night. They behave quite differently from Dr. Sauer's blackcaps, however.

Under a starlit sky during the autumn migration season, Dr. Fromme's thirty-four robins, in cages in which direction was automatically recorded, tried to fly off towards the south-west, the normal compass point for their migratory flight. They were not in the least disturbed when the sky was heavily overcast, but behaved in exactly the same way, as indeed they did even when Dr. Fromme put the cages in a darkened room. Evidently their compass still worked in spite of the thick walls of the room.

But, when he repeated the experiment in a windowless chamber with walls of nine inches of reinforced concrete, there was a surprise. The birds began by duly fluttering towards the south-west, but then they fluttered south, west or even east. Something must have disturbed them. Obviously they could now discern their mysterious signpost only very dimly and uncertainly.

That suggested to Dr. Fromme the idea of moving his robins into a steel strong-room enclosed on all sides. As he suspected they would, the birds whirred about in confusion and were incapable of any orientation. When the strong-room was opened they recovered a slight tendency to fly south-west again.

Thus a strong-room can deprive European robins of their mysterious signpost, and if the door is opened, a small part of these seemingly magical powers returns. Now, an enclosed steel chamber can weaken an external magnetic field and, in the form of a Faraday's cage, can completely screen off an electric field. This suggested that the birds' capacity for orientation was connected with the earth's magnetic field, for it was perfectly conceivable that this could have much the same effect on it as it has on a compass needle.

So Dr. Fromme tried to upset the robins' assumed magnetic sense by hanging small magnets round their heads. But this did not disturb them in the least. He also set up a two-metre magnet coil in the strong-room in such a way that he could shift the natural magnetic field by 90 degrees.

Now, if robins found their way by a magnetic field, they

would have been diverted by this from south-west to north-west. But they were not diverted. All experiments with magnetic fields proved fruitless. It is therefore claimed that the magnetic hypothesis put forward by other scientists must be dropped.

The next idea was that the solution might be found, not in a magnetic, but in an electrical field or in electro-magnetic radiation. Attention has repeatedly been drawn to the fact that migrant birds and homing pigeons can be deflected by the beam of powerful radar transmitters.

Migratory birds found their way about the world for millions of years before transmitters were erected by human hands, so Dr. Fromme is now looking for natural sources of radiation.

Suspicion first centred on the electro-magnetic short wave radiation which reaches us from space, particularly from the centre of the Milky Way. Were Dr. Fromme's robins sensitive to this? He went into the matter and came to the following conclusions.

In the course of the day the Milky Way passes across the sky just like the sun and the stars. Thus a source of radiation in the Milky Way in conjunction with the internal clock could be used as a compass in the same way as the sun and stars. In that case, when their internal clock was put forward or back six hours by means of the stratagem already described, the birds would be diverted to a wrong course. But that does not happen. They fly south-west as usual, even when their internal clock is wrong. That disposes of all theories about cosmic radiation.

So there is nothing for it but for the zoologists to enquire of physicists, geophysicists, ionosphere specialists and electrical technicians what other sources of radiation might be involved.

A ray of light on the problem may be thrown by the following. In 1960 Dr. James R. Heirtzler, the specialist on geomagnetism at the Lamont Observatory in the United States, discovered so-called micro-pulsations. These are electromagnetic waves of really astronomical proportions. The wavelength of the longest so far measured is 30 million kilometres, about a hundred times the distance from the earth to the moon.

A single vibration of this type of electro-magnetic radiation takes 100 seconds, but its strength is as minute as its dimensions are huge. The strength of its magnetic field is 100 million times less than that of a small toy magnet. The same applies to the strength of the electric field combined with it. Yet it is capable of penetrating the terrestrial globe. Many things about its origin and properties are still obscure. It cannot be claimed that it acts as guide to our robins, homing pigeons, limpets, toads, cats, mice, seagulls, bats and many other animals. It is merely quoted here as an example to show how inadequate is our present knowledge of the forces affecting the animal kingdom.

14
THE POWER OF INSTINCT

Provocative Feathers

INSTINCT, that antithesis of reason which in many situations impels living creatures to take action that saves their lives, long seemed to obey laws incomprehensible to the human intelligence. Nevertheless discoveries have been made in recent years which permit us a first glimpse into the world of animal psychology. Especially fruitful results have been obtained from experiments in which animals were placed in extreme situations in which they could not react according to a pattern and instead behaved in the most extraordinary way.

Professor Konrad Lorenz performed an experiment on the turkey-duck that became famous. He held in his hand a loudly quacking mallard duckling and showed it to a mother turkey-duck that was waddling past with her tribe of young. The little duckling's cries of distress put the turkey-duck in a state of high excitement. She flew at the professor, cackling loudly, struck at him with her wings, snatched the duckling from him, and made off with it out of the danger-zone as fast as she could.

The liberated duckling now tried to make friends with the turkey-duck's tribe of young, whereupon she promptly switched over to aggression. She would have killed the little creature she had just risked her life to save but for the professor's intervention.

How is this highly inconsistent behaviour of the turkey-duck to be explained? Professor Lorenz ascribes it to two different instinctual reactions occurring in close succession.

The turkey-duck responded to the duckling's cry of distress because the latter resembled that of her own young.

But the duckling's plumage was of a different colour, and a few moments later she identified it as a stranger with aggressive intentions. Primitive duck species like the turkey-duck do not know their children individually as do other types of duck, but respond only to specific stimuli that rouse various maternal instincts.

Here is another example. Professor Lorenz trained a wild European robin to come to him fearlessly and eat out of his hand. When he put on dark horn-rimmed spectacles the bird failed to recognise him and flew away in alarm.

If a male European robin is approached by a rival, it displays its red breast, raises its tail, sways from side to side and then either flies at the other or takes to flight, depending on whether it feels the stronger or weaker party.

The astonishing thing is that the European robin that fails to recognise its benefactor if he puts on a pair of spectacles identifies as a rival a small tuft of red breast-feathers held in front of it on a wire and agitated to and fro, and promptly begins its display of threats and aggression.

The mere stimulus of red feathers being agitated makes it assume its combative pose, just as a red traffic light causes a driver to put his foot on the brake, irrespective of whether traffic is coming or not.

Press-button Reaction

For every species there are certain phenomena – characteristic of their environment, however insignificant they may be in themselves – that release the full force of some reaction as if at the press of a button.

A budgerigar reared alone in a cage will readily adopt as a companion a blue and white table-tennis ball. It takes it to be the head of one of its own kind who has come to keep it company. But the ball must be put between the bars of the cage exactly on a level with its head. If it is lower, it makes the bird obviously uneasy. If it is higher, it frightens it. If it drops to the ground, the bird grows silent, and behaves as budgerigars do if one of them dies in the cage. It mourns.

Professor Otto Koehler, of Freiburg University, had the following experience. While he was cycling down a country path his back wheel went into a rabbit-hole and buckled. As he was a long way from home, he decided to ride on, in spite of the uncomfortable up-and-down motion. He noticed to his surprise that an inquisitive young rabbit that emerged from the hole obstinately followed him and refused to be shooed away.

Being a zoologist, he immediately saw why. An innate mechanism had been triggered off. A young rabbit will follow anything with a hopping motion, whether it is his mother or a professor on a damaged bicycle.

During the war Professor Niko Tinbergen, now of Oxford University, had a similar experience. He was cycling through a wood when a young fawn insisted on trotting along behind him. It had mistaken the white-painted rear mudguard for the white spot on its mother's posterior. The impulse to follow was released simply by the white patch on the rear of a moving object.

If a pair of black bathing-trunks is waved in the presence of jackdaws or crows, to them it is a sign to go to the defence of a stolen young one. Cawing furiously, they fly at the unsuspecting offender, though only very exceptionally do they attack him with the beak. Sometimes elderly women walking with a black handbag in a park are attacked by crows.

Any mobile object, a splinter, a scrap of paper, a flower petal, will be pounced on by a young toad if it is between two millimetres and eight inches long. Only gradually does it learn to distinguish between the edible and inedible.

A male house-fly walking on a light-coloured wooden rafter takes every dark nail-head to be a female, pounces and only then discovers its error. It never learns by experience, and invariably makes the same mistake.

Such instinctive mistakes are sometimes exploited in nature for quite different purposes. The colour and shape of the

The eye of a bee consists of 2,500 separate facets.

The cat possesses an uncanny homing instinct. Just as unfathomable as her eyes is her capacity for finding her way out of a labyrinth.

The artificial starlit sky in a planetarium. The black silhouette is the projector. Migrating birds orient to the stars it projects as well as they do by the real stars.

labellum of some South American orchids attracts tropical wasps just like a wasp female. The males go through the motions of copulation on these petals and thus transfer the pollen.

Flight from dangerous enemies is also instinctive in many animals. It is often triggered off simply by a pair of staring eyes. Chaffinches, house-sparrows, yellow-hammers, even hens, fly at the mere sight of an owl's eyes, whether these are in the head of a live owl or are dummies 'painted' on butterfly wings. The peacock-butterfly scares away its enemy by simulating the latter's enemy which would like to eat it.

Fly Routs Turkeys

To make a closer study of fright reactions, Dr. Wolfgang Schleidt carried out some interesting experiments on turkeys at the Max Planck Institute of Physiology of Behaviour. If a cardboard dummy of a bird of prey in flight is catapulted over a turkey-farm, it causes a wild panic, even if the turkeys have never seen a bird of prey. But not the slightest alarm is caused by a swallow flying across the yard. Because of this it was assumed that turkeys instinctively distinguished the shapes of flying birds of prey from those of harmless birds, or, in other words, that 'knowledge' of the silhouettes of the many buzzards, falcons, hawks, sparrow-hawks and eagles, and also of those of pigeons, swallows, storks and every other type of bird, was firmly anchored in their germ plasm.

In reality things are much simpler. Dr. Schleidt established in 1961 that the panic-causing stimulus was any object dark enough to stand out clearly against the sky that moved relatively slowly in relation to its size. In other words, any dark object with a slow angular velocity in the sky is suspect, whether it is the dummy of a sparrow or a bird of prey, and no matter what its shape may be; it makes no difference whether it is a cross, a circle or a triangle. But it causes panic only if it is not catapulted across the yard too quickly.

As birds of prey soar and wheel slowly at a great height, their appearance causes alarm at once. The annual return of the storks caused great alarm among the turkeys at first, but they quickly learnt that there was nothing to fear from them. Also they have grown used to aircraft of all current types, and now panic only at the relatively rare sight of a helicopter.

On the other hand, a pigeon solemnly gliding over the yard at the mating season can cause a panic, and so can a hen's feather slowly drifting in the wind. Absurd as it may sound, a fly crawling across a white ceiling also made turkeys panic. After all, it was a dark, slow-moving object.

Thus instinctive modes of behaviour, in contrast to acquired modes, can be released by simple stimuli. There is present in the nervous system a hereditary pattern of nerve pathways which enable the animal to receive these stimuli and automatically interpret them in the brain in such a way that nerve signals are transmitted to the muscular system, thus bringing about an appropriate reaction to the stimulus.

Unreliable Maternal Instinct

If such a pattern is not present in the nervous system, no appropriate reaction by the animal occurs – even in situations in which, from our human point of view, it seems obvious that it should.

An example of this is provided by a blackcap that has hatched out a cuckoo's egg in addition to her own. A few days after leaving the shell the little interloper, following a system of innate modes of action and reaction that is as marvellous as it is cruel, sets systematically about tipping its foster-brothers and sisters out of the nest. It creeps under them, clamps them firmly on its back between its wings and climbs out on to the edge of the nest, where it unseats the unwilling passenger with a bucking movement.

Usually the unfortunate youngster is deposited overboard. Sometimes, however, it is left lying on the edge of the nest. In that case the most astonishing thing is what happens next, which is nothing at all. The mother blackcap settles in the nest again without making the slightest effort to rescue her baby lying helplessly before her eyes on the edge of the nest. She lets it die of hunger and cold, though a single beak movement would be sufficient to tip it back into safety.

The blackcap's instincts enable it to fly all the way to Africa, navigating by the stars, but make no provision for the rescue of its children in such a situation. In contrast to other animals, it is 'too stupid' to learn from experience or exercise rational judgment in this situation.

Dr. P. Karli observed a similar helplessness among rat mothers. As a rule rats kill mice whenever they come across them, but at the time when they have young they behave differently. The emergence of the maternal instinct suddenly causes them to pick up mice and tend them lovingly, taking them to be young rats.

If they come across a mouse at this season, they pick it up in their mouth and take it to their nest. This is an extremely harmful procedure for, as soon as the mouse has recovered from its fright, it takes the baby rats for young mice and makes off with them. But the rat's maternal love of the mouse that is pillaging her nest persists. Dr. Karli once saw a rat carrying in its mouth a mouse which was carrying in its mouth a baby rat.

The same behaviour continued with all the rat's succeeding litters. Under the compulsion of her instincts and the stimuli that released them, she was incapable of learning to remove the 'cuckoo' from her nest.

This example illustrates the unreliability of the seasonal maternal instinct in animals. A small mistake, the misinterpretation of a stimulus, or merely a situation not provided for in nature's plan – and maternal affection can switch to murder or cannibalism.

A wrong odour, perhaps because it has been touched by a human hand, causes a golden hamster promptly to devour its young. If the mother animal is very hungry, she will bite into the young one's belly while severing the umbilical cord. A premature revival of the mating instinct will cause sparrows to tip their young out of the nest. Sometimes, indeed, an error in behaviour is enough. If, for instance, a young golden hamster remains asleep while its brothers and sisters are sucking, the mother assumes it to be a stranger and calmly eats it.

Not all animals manage to switch so completely as the mother polar bear from tremendous voracity to devoted nursing of the young. According to Dr. K. M. Schneider, director of the Leipzig zoo, who died in 1955, it builds its young a snow cave five feet wide and four feet high, approached through a sloping tunnel ten feet long and two feet three inches high and closed by a door of ice. Even so, if the new-born animal were left to itself it would die of cold, for it weighs only nineteen pounds, and is practically naked until its fur grows. So its mother lies on her side, holding it in the curve of her foreleg, keeping it gently covered with her other huge paw and the fur of her throat, and warming it with her breath besides.

Irresistible Dummies

Instinctive reactions of animals can be produced by dummies, provided they produce the stimulus required by nature. Chicks, for instance, will follow a piece of wood slowly revolving six inches above the ground on a rotating arm if it is surrounded by a thick woollen fringe while warmth is provided by a small infra-red lamp and a loudspeaker emits continuous clucks.

Professor Tinbergen obtained striking results when investigating the stimuli that trigger off the begging response in young gulls, causing them to stretch out their little heads and gaping beaks when the parents return to the nest with food. Was it personal recognition or the sight of the food?

It turned out to be neither. The professor established that the stimuli were the following: the red spot on the lower part of the parents' beak, the contrast between it and something light, the slanting position of the beak in regurgitating the food, the down and up movement, and finally the narrowing of the beak with the downward inclination for feeding.

If each one of these stimuli is separately imitated by a dummy, the young gulls respond feebly to them but, if all are combined in a single dummy, the begging reaction is as vigorous as if the parents were returning to the nest.

Professor Tinbergen went a step further. He exaggerated to

This artificial clucking hen consisted of a swivel cross-beam, a loudspeaker, an infra-red lamp and a rectangular board with a wool fringe. The chicks followed it as if it were a real hen.

an unnatural extent the size and vividness of colour of the red spot, the colour contrast, the slanting position, the narrowness and the rhythm of movement. This resulted in exaggerated reactions among the young gulls. They stretched their necks, opened their beaks and chirped as never before.

If this dummy was held to the nest just when the mother gull, now tamed and trusting, reached it to feed her young, she was completely ignored for the paltry dummy that bore not the slightest resemblance to a bird and brought no food.

The parents are also guided by the strongest stimulus. The tasty morsel goes to the fledgling that opens its mouth widest and displays the most brilliant colour in its throat. Dr. Otto von Frisch, son of the celebrated authority on bees, one day had to put up with having fat mealworms stuffed into both his ears by a tame jackdaw that was suddenly overcome with the maternal instinct. It took the funnel-shaped ear for a beak begging for food.

Professor Tinbergen removed an oyster-catcher's nest together with the eggs and put in its place two artificial nests,

If a dummy has the right characteristics, young seagulls will beg from it more importunately than from the mother who brings them food.

in one of which he put the bird's real eggs, which are two inches long, light blue and flecked with grey, while in the other he put various dummy eggs in turn. The bird was most attracted by one dummy which was painted bright blue with big black spots and was as big as an ostrich egg. The bird tried frantically to sit on this huge object, though it kept slipping off, and completely ignored its real clutch which was right before its eyes. The compulsion of a super-normal stimulus drove it to go on trying to hatch the giant egg, though it could not keep its seat on it for a moment.

The Science of Human Vices

The part played by supernormal stimuli in human affairs should not be under-estimated. When millions of people pay their mite at the box-office merely to admire a shapely film star, in the view of many psychologists they are responding to the same phenomenon as the oyster-catcher with the giant egg.

Another example is appetite. Our supernormal urge to

consume food is encouraged by innumerable cunningly contrived stimuli. A science of human vices could be based on the principles which have come to light in experiments on animals.

But hunger and love are not the only primary impulses behind animal and human action, nor are they all merely physical. On the contrary, each separate instinct can be theoretically regarded as having its own laws, as Professor Lorenz says. Probably there are just as many instincts in man as there are basically distinct emotional impulses. This new territory in psychology has yet to be explored in detail – a highly complicated task, as with us rational beings most of the primary impulses are expressed only in very modified form. To quote one example, man has a very pronounced reaction to the childishly pretty. It has been shown experimentally that it is released by the typical head conformation of young children – arching brows, rounded cheeks, large eyes. The reaction is intensified by curls. The biological meaning of this is that it releases the instinct to care for small children and babies.

Being innate, it is also released by similar phenomena. Thus we feel many animals to be pretty whose shape of head has the same characteristics, for example, rabbits, squirrels and robins.

Walt Disney's deer Bambi quite definitely possesses these distinctly childish characteristics. In fact a whole industry, the manufacture of dolls, lives on supplying the innate release mechanism of man with supernormally pretty dummies.

Cichlid Matrimonial Squabble

Konrad Lorenz has discovered a principle underlying all these various instinctive patterns of behaviour that can be released by co-ordinated external stimuli and also by appropriate dummies.

The longer a behaviour pattern anchored in the animal's constitution is not exercised, the more it seeks an outlet. It forces the organism to seek out a situation that will provide the stimulus that will release the behaviour pattern, and the longer it has lain fallow the stronger is the impulse. At the same time there is a diminution in the quantity of threshold resistance that the releasing mechanism has to overcome before it can become effective, until a point is finally reached at which a substitute object can bring about the release, or it can even happen 'in the void'. There is a remarkable parallel here with behaviour patterns that depend on the state of fullness of hollow organs or the needs of the body tissues, such as hunger and thirst.

Professor Lorenz frequently observed that a well-fed tame starling which had caught no flies for some time would suddenly dart forward at a non-existent object in the air, return to its perch, go through the characteristic motions of killing and finally gulp down the non-existent object.

If several pairs of cichlids are put in a big aquarium, the individual couples demarcate their own territory from those of their neighbours. This leads to a lot of harmless biting and snapping along the border-line. Male and female always live peaceably and harmoniously together. But, if such a happy couple are put into a pool alone, for lack of constant clashes with disagreeable neighbours they start squabbling with each other. In the case of the very pugnacious species of mouth-breeding cichlids, these matrimonial disputes have a very unhappy ending. They live in rivers and lakes in Africa, and are very popular with tropical fish fanciers. In most types the female circulates with the eggs and hatched-out young ones in her mouth, and males often carry young or eggs also. When they are big enough the young swim about freely, but when danger threatens they scuttle back into the parental mouth.

If a couple of these fish, which are near relatives of *Perca fluviatilis*, have no other couples of their kind on whom to vent their pugnacity, the male kills his mate. Afterwards he appears to mourn for a long time and is said never to mate again. But the murder can be prevented by putting a mirror in the aquarium. This enables the quarrelsome male to work off his aggression by fighting himself every now and then, and domestic peace is thus assured.

Man behaves not dissimilarly. His frustration is at its worst when he is deprived, on an expedition or in a prisoner-of-war camp, for instance, of the ordinary opportunities of working off his normal, healthy aggression. An otherwise respected friend or companion who blows his nose or clears his throat can trigger off an incomprehensible outburst of rage – incomprehensible only to those not aware of the psychological laws of aggression and threshold values.

Experience shows that it can be an advantage to be able to assess correctly the threshold value of the aggressivity of one's immediate superior. When the atmosphere is tense, it is usually the innocent who bear the brunt. In the event of such an electrical discharge, increased caution is indicated. But the old hand knows that when the storm is over a distinctly benign atmosphere will prevail, and that in the shadow of a high threshold value he will be able to get away with a great deal.

Short-circuit

The situation becomes still more interesting when two contradictory instinctive modes of behaviour are released by external stimuli. The most frequent instance of this in animals is the conflict between the impulse to fight and that to run away. The result can be a kind of short-circuit, resulting in the strangest and most senseless actions.

If a rooster, for instance, does not know whether to fight or to run away, it goes through the motions of eating, even if there is nothing to eat anywhere in sight. In the same situation the stickleback begins digging a nest, the crane preens its feathers and the avocet behaves as if it wanted to go to sleep.

The male golden plover goes completely haywire. When an enemy approaches, the female, like many other ground-nesting birds, tries to distract its attention from the nest, but the male, instead of helping her to do this, is torn between aggression and fear, and makes as if to mate with the female – behaviour not at all calculated to avert the threatening danger.

These 'displacement' actions are always performed in a very weak and apparently casual, 'absent-minded' manner, as it were. In some cases the relief of tension may have its advantages, because at least one member of the couple ceases behaving provocatively. But a fox's appetite is hardly likely to be impaired by the strange behaviour of the male golden plover. Generally speaking, these displacement actions have no biological usefulness.

This phenomenon, too, occurs in man. Usually he calls the situation 'embarrassment'. He undertakes 'cleansing actions', that is to say, he scratches his head, or performs what are called acquired involuntary actions, such as easing his collar, tugging at his tie or lighting a cigarette.

Incidentally, smoking in tense situations is not a sign of adulthood or manliness, as many young people suppose, but an unconscious regression to the infantile co-ordination of movements found in sucking and thumb-sucking, and is a striking parallel to the senseless picking of the undecided rooster.

The fighting and running away instincts are not the only ones that come into conflict and hence lead to novel and as a rule completely senseless and apparently unaccountable behaviour. Many senseless actions of animals, and of men too, can be explained by two or more conflicting unconscious instinctual sources resulting in actions entirely beyond the control of reason. We shall return to this in the next chapter.

Further research in this sphere will certainly be of great importance to the understanding of neurotic symptoms in man. There are already signs of a bridge coming into being that will connect animal psychology with human psychiatry and the psychology of depth.

That is the significance of these words of Professor Erich von Holst who, after distinguished service as director of the Max Planck Institute for Physiology of Behaviour, died in the spring of 1962: 'The aim of our work on animals,' he stated, 'must be to obtain simple and easily intelligible models of behaviour, so that in the future, in combination with other branches of science, we may by our labours gain new knowledge in the sphere of psychotherapy, and thus be able to heal the psychological maladies of modern man, with all his incalculable impulses and desires, inner conflicts and inconsistencies.'

Evolutionary Origin

In the laughing-gull three emotional situations can simultaneously conflict with one another – aggression, the desire to run away and the desire to stay close together. The product of this mixture, strange to relate, is the courtship ceremonial. Professor Tinbergen describes what happens as follows. A male gull seeks out a nesting-place in the sand dunes. A slight hollow, or even only a human footprint, will suffice. If another laughing-gull approaches, the male stands stiffly at an oblique angle, with head raised and tail down, and utters a long screech.

Among laughing-gulls this is normally the threatening cry to scare away unwanted guests. Generally it causes other males to make off, but not the females, who take it as an invitation and promptly settle somewhere near the male.

Male and female both tilt forward like a see-saw, so that the head slants down and the tail up. This is normally the 'ready for action' position assumed before a fight, but male and female do not face each other directly as if about to go into action, but stand parallel, side by side, with their heads in the same direction, never looking at each other, at any rate directly.

A few seconds later first one and then the other assumes a proud posturing attitude, which also can serve either as the introduction to a fight or to intimidate an opponent. To strip it of its martial aspect, however, each bird turns its head away from the other at exactly the same moment and looks for some time in the opposite direction. This is a kind of flight from each other, except that they remain standing at the same spot and thus still demonstrate a rather vague feeling of solidarity. By fusing into a single gesture the desire to run away and the desire to stay together, they turn the initial threat into an attitude of conciliation.

Courtship ceremonial of the laughing-gull. *Left*, the threatening cry that entices the female. *Centre*, combative attitude adapted to courtship. *Right*, bashful averting of the head, conflict between attraction and instinctive urge to take flight.

To begin with, the female is very demure. She keeps her distance from the male, and betrays her anxiety by the extreme smoothness of her plumage. After both have gazed intently in opposite directions, the female cautiously turns her head towards the male, but the slightest movement on his part makes her turn away again.

As a rule the female stays for only a very short time and then grows uneasy and flies away. The male may succeed in calling her back, but generally she settles near another calling male. In gull colonies a female can often be observed visiting a whole series of courting males in rapid succession.

Sooner or later, however, she develops a preference for one particular male. She settles near him again and again, and each time they go through the same half-warlike, half-placatory approach ceremony. By degrees the aggressive postures grow less aggressive and the signs of fear more superficial. Gradually the female goes closer to the male and looks at him with unconcealed curiosity.

This process of habituation may be got through very quickly, or may last for several days and call for twenty or forty visits. But the ceremonial grows more and more cursory, the two begin to spend a great deal of time together, and finally the male produces evidence of his capacity as a potential paterfamilias – he feeds the female, to the accompaniment of many caresses. Mating takes place soon afterwards. Next year, after distant journeyings in which the two fly separately in the general swarm of gulls, the two are reunited without much formality. This has been demonstrated by the ringing of birds.

This is a good illustration of how instinctive rituals may have arisen in the animal kingdom. It is even more evident with another species of gull. The male herring-gull lures females in a rather different way. As soon as he feels he is being looked at by a female on the wing, he bends forward with an expansive gesture over a small depression in the ground and rhythmically nods his head. This bending-over-the-nest gesture is that of the female settling on her eggs. The rhythmical bobbing up and down of the head is a dance-like variation of the nest-building movement. In both cases an action in the void is 'ritualised' into a symbolic gesture.

The evolutionary origin of ritual gestures can be clearly recognised in the following. If a herring-gull inadvertently crosses the border of another herring-gull's nesting-place, the bird in possession pecks vigorously at the ground, angrily tears out a few blades of grass and small plants, and tosses them aside with a shake of the head. He thus makes it unmistakably plain to the intruder that his head is in danger of being just as roughly handled as the earth and that he is running the risk of having his wing or tail-feathers rumpled just as badly as the tufts of grass. Generally the intruder takes the hint and makes off.

Posturing in Man and Chimpanzee

'Displaced' attacks of this kind are not unknown to us human beings when we bang our fist on the table or hurl a chair into the corner in a rage.

The speech symbols with which animals communicate with each other by releasing a quite definite type of behaviour in the recipient arose from actual modes of behaviour at some time in the remote past. In the course of evolution the symbols became increasingly subtle, complicated and abstract in the case of many animals.

In the courtship ceremonial of ducks the originally practical actions underlying the individual dance figures can no longer be discerned. In the course of tens of thousands of years the most varied breeds of duck with the most varied instinctive modes of expression have crossed with each other too often, resulting in new modes of behaviour each time.

Every species and every breed of animal has a characteristic pattern of instinctual behaviour which distinguishes it from other species and breeds just as its bodily structure does. The more closely related two breeds are in bodily structure, colour of coat or feathers, functioning of internal organs and other characteristics, the more they resemble each other in their modes of behaviour, in so far as these are hereditary, firmly established in their genetic substance, and not acquired by any learning process. Thus the innate modes of behaviour of animals have been handed on from generation to generation for countless ages down to our own times, like the number of their teeth, the shape of their ribs and the development of their feet.

In some cases modes of behaviour dating from a remote past have survived more stubbornly than physical character-istics. We have already mentioned the farmyard geese which in certain situations repeatedly assure one another in their cackling language that they have absolutely no intention of flying, though they long ago lost the ability to do so.

Here is another example. It frequently happens that flies are born without wings. Radioactivity or other environmental influences have brought about an erratic change in their germ plasm, a mutation. This accounts for the absence of wing development in the fly pupa. Nevertheless these creatures regularly go through the motions of preening their non-existent wings.

Certain forms of behaviour in man have survived events in his natural history such as the loss of his fur and the transition to an upright carriage. If a man is put in a position in which a combative reaction is required of him, say in politics or in football, the tension of his muscular system rises immediately. He pushes his shoulders and chin forward, shuts his lips, raises his arms slightly and rotates them inwards. This corresponds exactly to the threatening posture of the male chimpanzee.

15

MIND AND BODY

Remote Control in the Poultry-yard

IN the grounds of the Max Planck Institute for Physiology of Behaviour near Munich there is a poultry-yard that is unique. At first glance there is nothing very unusual about it, but then one's attention is attracted by a number of radar-like directional antennae erected all round. Each transmits ultra-short radio waves to a particular chicken. The latter picks them up with a light transistor receiving set and an antenna concealed under its feathers.

At the beginning of the experiments the antennae were placed on their heads, making them look like imaginary Martians or creatures out of a Utopian novel, but their appearance at once reduced them to the lowest place in the pecking order, and if their status were to be maintained the aerial and receiver had to be concealed. From the receiver a pair of fine wires passes direct into the chicken's brain, where it works like an artificial nerve. When the apparatus is not working, everything in the poultry-yard goes on as usual. The wire has been painlessly inserted into the chickens' brain, and they feel nothing. But one press on the button and the picture changes.

A chicken which was cheerfully picking grains of corn suddenly lies down and goes to sleep. Another, which was eating with equal unconcern, suddenly stretches its neck and peers anxiously into the distance, as if a dog were running towards it. It grows more and more restless, shrinks together and leaps aside with a great cackling and flapping of wings, though no enemy is in sight.

Another, a miserable creature, normally irresolute in

Swallows assembled on telephone wires to set out together for distant lands look like musical notation. Their 'internal calendar' tells them the date when they must take off.

A salmon leap. Scent directs it on its course upstream.

This is how a mother redstart sees the hungry beaks of her young.

character, always giving way submissively to its fellows and relegated to the bottom of the social scale, suddenly stretches itself up proudly, struts to the most favoured feeding-places and impudently pecks its dumbfounded superiors out of the way.

What has happened? These three chickens are under radio remote control. Their transistor sets pick up signals which are then amplified and relayed by wire to their brain, where they behave like nerve currents from other regions of the brain, reporting sense impressions or feelings, such as 'I am tired and am going to sleep' or 'There's a dangerous dog rushing at us' or 'I'm the cock of the walk'. In each case the chicken responds to these artificially produced hallucinations as if they were realities.

Command Posts in the Nervous System

How can an artificial electric stimulus provoke in a chicken modes of behaviour as complex and intricate as going to sleep, running away from a dog or assuming the aggressive posture? A brief survey of the command structure of the nervous system will help towards making the phenomenon intelligible.

Command posts of the lowest echelon – innumerable nerves controlling a single muscle – are distributed all over the body. If these are stimulated by a natural or artificial electric current, the muscle in the leg of a frog, for example, reacts by twitching violently.

The next higher echelon in the chain of command lies in the spinal cord, where, for instance, the secondary nerve tracts from all the muscles of a leg converge. If a natural nerve impulse from higher up, or an artificial impulse from a wire, reaches this spot, the leg in question makes a natural walking movement. Thus several groups of muscles, those of a leg, for instance, are harmoniously co-ordinated by these 'nerve switchboards' in the spinal column.

The next higher control centre lies in the *medulla oblongata*, just below the brain. If this is stimulated with an electric current, the animal advances apparently normally with all its legs. Here, then, a signal produces the synchronised co-ordination of several limbs. The resulting locomotion is of course aimless and purposeless. So long as the electrical stimulus continues, the animal goes on advancing in the direction in which it was facing at the beginning of the experiment.

In the mid-brain there are other main nerve centres which co-ordinate the muscular system of the whole animal for complete modes of behaviour. Here the so-called elementary modes of behaviour are produced; for example, in the chicken, squatting, standing up, scratching with the foot, turning the head up,

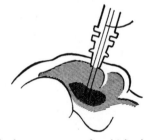

Cross-section through the upper part of a chicken's head. Two fine silver wires are inserted through the brain (shaded) into the mid-brain (darker shading) by means of stereotaxic apparatus.

down, right or left, preening itself, looking round, stretching its neck, uttering a cry of alarm or communicating by means of some other sound, and so on and so forth.

The late Professor Erich von Holst and his colleague Dr. Wolfgang Jechorek succeeded after protracted experiment at the Max Planck Institute for Physiology of Behaviour in producing these elementary modes of behaviour in chickens by artificial means – electrical stimulation of the appropriate regions of the mid-brain. The artificial nerves, silver wires as fine as hairs, were inserted in the mid-brain under an anaesthetic, and the birds felt no pain. They felt nothing even after they came round, for inside the brain there are no nerves sensitive to pain.

With the aid of delicate stereotaxic apparatus wires were inserted in all the regions of the mid-brain without the fowl's taking the slightest notice. They remained perfectly healthy and normal throughout, even if the artificial nerves were left in their brain for several years in the course of which they were subjected to artificial nerve stimulation hundreds of times.

Living Creature as Robot

Here is an example of a relatively simple experiment. The artificial nerve is inserted by means of the stereotaxic apparatus into a mid-brain region of the fowl from which, it turns out, 'interest in the right' can be aroused. If the electrical stimulus is very weak (not more than a few tenths of a volt are used) the animal stops still and looks sharply to the right. If the strength of the current is gradually increased, it begins, at first slowly and then faster and faster, to move to the right, gazing more and more intently in that direction, as if there were something important to be seen there. By activating another region of the brain 'interest in below' can be aroused. If the bird is standing on a table, bored, it begins by looking down at its feet. As the stimulus grows stronger it goes to the edge of the table and stretches its head down as far as it can, and finally it jumps to the ground.

Stimulation of another spot in the mid-brain causes it to turn its head sideways and get out of the way of something that is not there; in fact it behaves rather as it does when it makes way for a chicken of higher rank. Also its eye can be caused to water, as if it had something in it. It blinks, shakes its head vigorously and, when the stimulus is increased, scratches round the eye with its foot, apparently trying to remove a non-existent blade of grass. Stimulation of yet another spot makes it feel it has hurt its foot. It takes great care of it, limps severely and stands on the other leg.

All the other elementary modes of behaviour in the chicken's repertoire can be released by artificial stimuli in the same way. Examples are dropping a curtsey and at the same time giving the mating-call, making a gesture of apology by slightly raising its wings, picking grains of corn from the ground, drinking, ruffling the feathers, and drawing in the head; and there are many more besides.

There are many other regions in the mid-brain which are still higher in the chain of command. These are able to co-ordinate a series of elementary movements into 'complex modes

Signals transmitted over a radio antenna produce an agitated fighting mood in a chicken.

of behaviour'. A chain of elementary movements – ceasing to eat, looking around, walking about, a restless movement of the eyelids, yawning, settling down, ruffling the feathers, drawing in the head and closing the eyes – results in the complex be-haviour of going to sleep. Another chain – ceasing to eat, drawing oneself up, spitting out food, shaking the head and wiping the beak on the ground – results in a feeling of nausea.

Seeking out food and eating it, seeking out water and drink-ing, fleeing from predators on the ground, fleeing from pre-dators in the air, taking a hen to the nest, putting an inferior in its place, fighting an enemy of another species, mourning, triumphing and many other things are chains of separate elementary activities.

It is perfectly possible to induce a chicken to go to sleep by stimulating one after the other the nine elementary movements involved, but the complete series can be produced more simply by stimulating the appropriate higher control centre, by pressing a single button, so to speak.

Moreover, in that case the chicken acts rationally, as it were, in contrast to what happens when the lower centres in the *medulla oblongata* are stimulated. In the latter case it will, for instance, go on walking as long as the electrical stimulus continues, even if this means running into a wall or into the water. But when the higher centre, to which the five senses are connected, is stimulated the chicken takes its environment into account and carries out the orders given to it by way of the artificial nerve in accordance with what it sees, hears, feels, tastes and smells.

It may have a full belly but, if the 'hunger' button is pushed, it at once sets out in search of food, but what actually happens depends on external circumstances. It may make a detour round an obstacle, peck a rival out if its way or be pecked away itself and fail in its objective.

Whether the electrical stimulus reaches the region of the mid-brain concerned naturally from other areas of the brain or artificially by way of a silver wire, it awakens a need in the animal, gives it an aim, a mood, actually an hallucination.

The chicken is of course not really hungry, thirsty or tired. But if man artificially stimulates the hunger, thirst or fatigue centre of its mid-brain, it reacts exactly as if the centre had been stimulated by way of its real bodily nerves, which normally report the presence of real hunger, thirst or fatigue.

To the mid-brain, that wonderful, completely automatic control centre in the living creature, the source of a stimulus makes no difference. It cannot distinguish between true and false. It deals with every electrical stimulus that reaches it, and passes down the necessary orders to the muscular system by way of the appropriate nerve tracks in the manner dictated by heredity.

That is why Professor von Holst was able to produce all sorts of artificial hallucinations in chickens. By stimulating one particular region of the mid-brain he was able to make a cock feel threatened by a perfectly peaceable, harmless, unsuspecting and much weaker hen. It stooped, arched its wings, rumpled its ruff and attacked the surprised animal with spur and beak. If no hen was about, it searched until it found one to act as a 'lightning conductor' for its rage and paranoia. In this mood it did not even fight shy of attacking a dog or a human being.

Most dramatic of all was the behaviour of a hen which reacted to stimulation of a certain point in the mid-brain by furiously defending her non-existent chicks against an equally non-existent hawk. She ruffled her feathers, dashed about in small circles and let out piercing squawks. In this situation she actually accepted strange chickens that were foisted on her, though normally she pecked them away. But now she took them lovingly under her wings and was ready to fight to the death defending them against an imaginary air attack.

These artificially produced hallucinations represent practically the same phenomenon as that in mentally disturbed humans whose persecution mania centre is stimulated by a 'short-circuit' in the brain though there is no reason whatever for it in reality.

There are plenty of indications that the artificially produced hallucinations in chickens are genuine. In other words, when they jump out of the way cackling noisily, they really see a non-existent dog just as if it were real. One experiment in particular confirmed Professor von Holst in this opinion. In the mid-brain of a cock he stimulated the centre indicating 'a ground enemy is approaching' and slowly increased the current. The cock began by straining its neck and peering into the distance. Then it nervously shrank into itself, as if the dog were dangerously close. At that moment the professor switched off the current. The cock was obviously completely nonplussed, and looked about him as if to say: 'What on earth has become of the dog? It can't have been spirited away into thin air.'

Professor von Holst and Dr. Jechorek actually succeeded in transmitting sensations from one chicken to another. They inserted in the mid-brain of each an artificial nerve at the point indicating 'fear of a dog'. They then put each into a separate room and with an amplifier established a direct connexion between the two creatures' brains. When a dog on a lead was taken into one of the rooms, both chickens fluttered up the wall, squawking in alarm.

Contradictory Orders

If it is possible to activate instinctive behaviour in a fowl in the manner just described, it must also be possible to activate two modes of behaviour simultaneously. Professor von Holst experimented with this, with very surprising results.

Two pairs of wires instead of one were introduced into the fowl's brain in places governing different modes of behaviour. The experimenters began with combining two different elementary actions, 'pick on the ground' and 'pay attention to the right'. The result, as expected, was 'pick on the ground to the right'. Similarly 'squat' plus 'keep on the watch with extended neck' resulted in squatting with extended neck. Similarly, 'stand up' could be combined with 'cackle' and 'squat' with 'preen the back feathers', and other elementary actions that were not inconsistent with each other could also be combined.

If two elementary actions which run counter to each other are released simultaneously, such as 'stand up' and 'sit down', or 'pick on the ground' and 'preen the back feathers', the situation is more complicated, and the chicken is put in a state of conflict. Both actions break down before they have properly begun; they 'jam', or alternate in rapid succession. If 'pick on the ground', for instance, is combined with 'keep a good look-out for distant danger', the animal makes a few picking motions, jerks its head up and looks quickly round in all

223

directions, again picks a few grains and then jerks its head up, and so on until the stimulus is switched off.

It may happen that only one impulse breaks through while the other is repressed. Strangely enough, in such cases it is the depressive impulses that generally get the better of the pleasurable ones. Thus, 'comfortably ruffle the feathers' is repressed by 'shrink nervously into oneself'. If the two stimuli are switched off simultaneously, the repressed impulse finds a belated outlet. In a flash the shrunken fowl ruffles up into a contented tuft of feathers.

The 'run away', 'squawk with fright', 'feel cold', 'warn against enemies' and 'scold' stimuli similarly get the better of all those associated with pleasure and contentment, but the latter break through afterwards as if they have been stored up. A cock, for instance, will promptly throw off its fear or humility, stand upright, flap its wings and crow triumphantly. Pleasurable excitement is suppressed even if it is provoked by a considerably stronger electric current than is anxiety. Pleasure predominates only when a specific difference in the strength of the current is reached. This provides science with an excellent means of measuring the strength of an animal's hereditary instincts.

Origin of Novel Modes of Behaviour

Professor von Holst went further, and simultaneously imposed two complex modes of behaviour on a chicken. This is a highly complicated business, for every complex mode of behaviour consists of a sequence of separate elementary actions each of which is overlaid by another simultaneous elementary action. Until all the details of this have been understood, we are faced with as many discords as on a piano on which two pianists are each playing a different piece.

Hence, with one single exception, the results of these experiments were disappointing. Either no results were obtained, or else exceedingly curious modes of behaviour obviously devoid of purpose or meaning.

224

The only success obtained so far resulted from the combination of the two activities 'squatting' and 'running away'. Artificial stimulation in this case produced a phenomenon which offers a striking parallel to the 'displaced' actions mentioned in the previous chapter.

Here too the outcome was an entirely new type of behaviour. On being given the two artificial stimuli, the squatting chicken displayed a state of great alarm. It stood up, went this way and that as if it did not know where to go, stopped dead and then jumped aside in terror. That is its normal behaviour when evading a swooping bird of prey.

Professor von Holst produced the same effect by subjecting it to one of these two stimuli artificially and the other naturally. He terrified the creature by showing it a barking dog while commanding it by artificial means to squat. It showed terror, not of the dog, but of an imaginary hawk.

This experiment demonstrates that artificial stimulation of the mid-brain releases real and not pseudo-impulses and instinctive actions. The artificial wire in the chicken's brain is completely equivalent to its real nerves and works in the same way, except that it does not emanate from other regions of the brain and is not anchored in the grand design of the hereditary substance but depends on the will of a human experimenter.

Atlas of the Mind

Similar experiments have meanwhile been carried out at the Max Planck Institute for Physiology of Behaviour on ducks, geese, reptiles and insects. With the aid of a special technique, Dr. Jechorek actually succeeded in exercising remote control of fish and controlling their behaviour by pressing a button. In every case artificial stimulation of a particular point in the mid-brain produced identical behaviour in the creature, provided of course that external and internal circumstances were the same.

If they are not the same, modifications occur. One possible source of disturbance is the impact on the animal of a new sense impression, which may repress, weaken, strengthen or change the reaction to the artificial electrical stimulus. Also, frequent repetition may accustom the animal to the artificial stimulus, in which case the threshold value for the instinctive response rises, and ultimately the animal no longer reacts at all. The reciprocal influence of a number of sense impressions, instinctive actions and habits is the reason why the experiments described are so extraordinarily difficult to carry out with precision. The worker can never tell for certain what state of mind the animal is in at any particular moment.

Is a chicken picking up grains of corn because it is hungry, or because it is jealous of others that are doing so? Its reaction to an artificial stimulus which tells it to adopt an aggressive attitude to its neighbours will differ accordingly. In the first case it will at most interrupt its eating for a few quick sideways pecks, while in the second case it will adopt a fighting posture and forget all about eating in the excitement of the fray.

When all is said and done, in spite of all these complications an animal running about in the yard and acting in accordance with an experimenter's instructions turns out to be a precisely functioning physical mechanism, though a highly complicated one, in the natural structure of which man has brought about artificial changes. We can hazard a comparison with another branch of science, and describe all the numerous motor points in the mid-brain, all the minute nerve systems crowded together in it, as 'particles of the mind', the structure of which man is just beginning to analyse and investigate.

It is such particles of the mind that in certain situations cause a chicken to adopt a militant attitude, contain the rules that govern the duelling of the viper, the courtship ceremonial of the drake, the whispers of the jackdaw 'in love', the blackcap's navigation by the stars, the incubator bird's central heating and cooling system and the archer-fish's method of marksmanship.

In 1960 Professor von Holst had begun compiling a three-dimensional atlas of the mind particles in the mid-brain of the chicken, in order to establish the whereabouts of all the various centres of behaviour and their spatial relationships with one another. He succeeded in cataloguing 150 altogether. But that was only a beginning. He calculated that with the most intensive efforts it would be impossible to complete the picture of the chicken's brain alone before 1980. After his premature death, that now depends on his work being taken up and continued by a worthy successor.

Rat Addict

An observer brought face to face with all these things cannot avoid a feeling of discomfort, if not actual horror.

Is it not all really a higher type of cruelty to animals? Is it not sacrilege to regard the mental activities of animals as the consequence of purely material processes? Are not powers being conjured up here which may escape from the control of human reason as easily as the forces in the atom, bringing in their wake catastrophic effects for all mankind?

Light on the feelings of animals under the artificial stimulation we have described is thrown by the work of Dr. James Olds, Professor of Psychology at the University of Michigan. He succeeded in discovering the 'pleasure centre' in the mid-brain of rats. Whenever he gave a rat an artificial electrical stimulus of eighty micro-amperes, five volts, and one second's duration, it uttered squeaks of delight. Later he made it walk along a runway which ended in a T fork. Whenever it took the right-hand fork he gave it an electric shock in the pleasure centre. After that it always turned to the right, even if it was very hungry and a trough full of food was visible on the left.

Professor Olds gave the rat a lever to close a contact which enabled it to stimulate its pleasure centre whenever it liked, a fact which it grasped very quickly. No one was prepared for what happened next. It took to giving itself an electric shock at regular intervals of four seconds. It gave up eating, drinking and sleeping. Like an addict who cannot give up his morphine, it went on working the contact over and over again – 24,000 times in a single day, as was established by means of an automatic counter.

Even if regions of the brain other than the pleasure centre are stimulated in chicken, for instance, they show by their health and whole behaviour that they do not suffer under these experiments. Professor von Holst intended to experiment with fine silver wires in his own brain to gain deeper insight into these complex phenomena, but he never got to that.

It is true that the insertion of fine wire filaments destroys some nerve-cells in the brain, but so few that its functioning is not affected. In any case many brain cells are destroyed or die off every day in adult living creatures, and are not replaced. In man the number is about 300,000 of a total of about 14,000 million, and in the chicken or rat the number is correspondingly high.

The effect of artificial stimulation on the animal can best be envisaged as follows. If a bird in a tree catches sight of a marten, or another time perhaps only hears its rustling, if it perhaps detects its approach only by a vibration of the branches, or if it grows nervous in the dark and only dreams of a marten, in all four cases electrical stimuli travel to one and the same centre from four different regions of the brain by four different nerve tracks, and the bird's reaction is always the same – 'a marten – I must get away from here'.

If man inserts a wire into this mid-brain centre and transmits to it an electric current similar to the nerve impulse, the bird has exactly the same experience, though this time without real cause. As in a bad dream, one might say.

Long-range Purpose

A more difficult problem is that of the connexion between the mental and material spheres. But it is only very superficially that it is a problem. The problems, methods and aims of every exact science are necessarily material in nature, because a scientist can work only with things he can see, feel, or in some way measure or observe. He is always aware that with his skill he can comprehend only the material side of creation, and the brain and nervous system of animals and man are included in that. Nerve fibres and nerve currents are material, and are therefore accessible to scientific investigation.

But that part of being that lies beyond all nerves and electrical currents and other perceptible things remains inaccessible to human science. This truth is increasingly driven home by the labours of the scientists. How senseless, stupid and primitive animals used to seem until scientists made evident to the world the magic garden of animal psychology. How vast are the problems the ever-growing multiplicity and magnitude of which seem to put them permanently beyond our reach, the problems which have only just become discernible behind the relatively few that have been solved.

And again, the real mental sphere has not yet been touched by the scientist. Professor von Holst actually believed that it would remain inaccessible to him to all eternity. Mind particles have certainly been discovered, and man has thereby climbed a rung higher on the ladder of knowledge, but he is as far away as ever from understanding the nature of mind. Even the recently acquired knowledge about physical atoms has not made clear what matter and energy are. Our self-awareness is a phenomenon that eludes scientific investigation. 'I hear a sound', 'I am glad' – how can things like that be dealt with experimentally?

The scientist does not ask himself the question 'What is the use of it all?' He is interested 'only in what holds the world together in its innermost parts', quite apart from any practical application.

In the case of the physiology of behaviour, the science of the connexion between the behaviour of animals and the physi-ology of their nervous systems, the future prospects are so striking that Professor Konrad Lorenz and Professor Erich von Holst began many years ago considering the further implica-tions of their labours.

They decided that artificial stimulation of the brain must be used solely for the purpose of investigating the nervous system and the instincts, and never to increase the working capacity of animals. They also decided that it would be criminal to influence the thoughts and the commissions and omissions of men by applying artificial stimuli to their brain. It is, of course, perfectly possible that a totalitarian regime might one day attempt such an outrage.

On the other hand, there are some very positive aspects to set against these deplorable negative possibilities. This new branch of science may one day succeed in unravelling the connexion between the nervous system and the hereditary instincts and thus in the distant future put new tools into the hands of the psychotherapist, thereby vastly extending the range of present-day depth psychology and psychiatry and providing firm foundations for effective therapy.

It seems not inconceivable that the future may lay bare the reason behind the unreason of human behaviour, as expressed in the last resort in the nuclear armaments race which against all reason has led the world to the edge of the abyss. In the words of Konrad Lorenz, the present world situation is, among other things, attributable to the fact that by artificial means man has himself created an environment to which by nature he is not mentally adjusted — a situation that in the past has led to the extinction of living creatures.

Nevertheless students of behaviour still nourish the hope that it may be possible to clarify and explain the causes of men's irrationality, and thereby point the way to adjustment to the world situation.

The Electronic Tortoise

Another interesting prospect held out by all this work on the physiology of behaviour is the artificial reproduction of the nervous systems of animals. The first phase would be the construction of robots which behaved like animals, and the next would turn to account the experience gained by constructing still more efficient electronic brains.

What is in mind here is illustrated by Hans Kretz's work at the Technical University in Vienna. Kretz constructed a robot on the pattern of Pavlov's celebrated dog. The pattern of the latter's behaviour was as follows. When it had had enough to eat and was tired, it went to sleep. Eventually it awoke and began examining its surroundings, first out of curiosity, and then to find more food.

If a bell was always rung when food was put in its bowl, it soon realised that the sound meant the presence of food and made straight for the bowl; also its salivary glands began secreting, irrespective of whether there was food in the bowl or not. Pavlov called this process the production of a conditioned reflex.

If the dog was disappointed several times by finding no food in its bowl when the bell rang, it soon ceased to react to the acoustic stimulus. It approached the bowl again only after it had been left in peace for some time.

Hans Kretz's robot, which behaves just like Pavlov's dog, is about ten inches long, four inches wide and four inches high. It runs on three wheels, is powered by two electric motors which can take it wherever it wants to go, and is known as an artificial tortoise. It possesses three sense organs – a photo-electric cell to see with, a microphone to hear with and an electrical contact to serve as the organ of touch.

Inside it is a small electronic brain that works on principles theoretically believed to be those of an animal's nervous system. If the robot behaved exactly like a living animal, it would prove that the theoretical assumptions were correct.

Altogether it contains a battery as a source of energy, eighteen transistors, nineteen relays and numerous low-voltage neon-glow lamps, diodes and heat conductors. They can amplify, add, differentiate, integrate, feed back, store up, count and delay the 'sense' stimuli received. They make the automaton an independent system, able appropriately to synchronise its programme of action with the changing impressions received from its environment.

231

To enable us to understand how it is possible to imitate natural nervous systems by means of electrical control elements, let us glance at what happens in our body if, for instance, we are pricked with a pin. Professor Friedrich Bonhoeffer, Director of the Max Planck Institute for Physical Chemistry, played an important part in research into such matters until his death in 1957.

The pin-point touches a tactile fibre in the skin originating in a sensory nerve cell sensitive to pressure. As a result of complicated molecular processes in the tactile fibre, an electric current is produced, the strength of which is strictly proportionate to the violence of the prick.

A telephone engineer would say that such a current was useless, for the human nervous system contains jamming stations which would distort and drown the signal in the human brain, giving it false information which might have the most devastating consequences. But to prevent this from happening nature resorts to a stratagem. After the current has passed through the nucleus of the nerve cell into the 'high power cable', and about half a millimetre along the latter, it is transformed into a series of short current impulses.

The stronger the stimulus current is, the faster does the mysterious coding apparatus flash its impulses. The message is now conveyed, not by the strength of the current, but by the speed of the transformation of the impulses – a technique by which interference is eliminated.

At intervals of every few millimetres along the 'high power cable' there are 'amplifier stations' at which line losses are made up. In man there are about 800 of such amplifier stages in a single 'cable' between finger-tip and brain. The speed at which signals travel along the nerves can be as much as 390 feet per second.

Up to 1,000 impulses a second can be transmitted by a nerve fibre, a high rate which, however, is not sufficient for many purposes. In these cases nature uses several nerve fibres in parallel. Each fibre takes over the transmission of a definite share of the signals, rather as each piston in an engine performs one stroke in a definite cycle. The finger-tip is not, however, connected with the brain by one continuous fibre leading all the way from the finger-tip; information about the

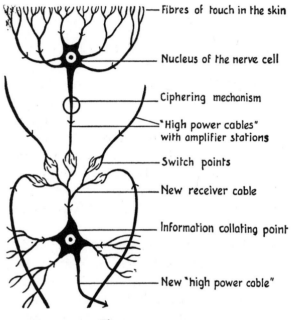

- Fibres of touch in the skin
- Nucleus of the nerve cell
- Ciphering mechanism
- "High power cables" with amplifier stations
- Switch points
- New receiver cable
- Information collating point
- New "high power cable"

The nervous system.

pin-prick has in fact to pass through several control-points in the spinal cord, the *medulla oblongata* and the mid-brain, at each of which the 'cable' through which the current impulse has just passed comes to an end. Here it touches the tip of another line leading back to the nucleus of another nerve cell.

At this point the information coming in is decoded into a faithful electrical reproduction of the strength and duration of the pin-prick.

Messages Collated

Before the message is recorded into impulses for further transmission, an important event takes place; other messages are received on other lines from other regions of the nervous system. Some of these are similar (those from adjacent tactile cells, for instance), but others are very different (e.g., those from definite regions of the brain which increase or reduce the sensation of pain). All these meet our original message, and are now capable of being collated and edited in a variety of ways.

The nerve cell at this point can strengthen, weaken or completely block the message from the previous nerve fibre. It can also choose which of several messages it will pass on, and finally it can combine, add, subtract or multiply the messages by each other – a staggering feat to be performed by a structure of such minute proportions. Man is just beginning to be able to tackle mathematical problems of this kind with the aid of electronic computers which fill whole rooms. But two, three or four nerve-cell combinations with feed-back loops and other connexions are able to undertake very tricky mathematical calculations.

In all this the messages received from the outer world undergo very great changes and soon become impossible to follow. At the beginning of the process there are light- and sound-waves, for instance, and it all ends with the brain's understanding that a fly is buzzing about the room. In between there is a great deal of chemistry, mathematics and physics.

Hans Kretz's problem was to construct an electronic brain capable of such behaviour-mathematics. As it is at present impossible to trace anatomically and imitate the complicated nerve connexions in the body of an animal, another method had to be chosen.

He therefore took as his starting-point the existing technique of constructing electronic brains and worked out the theoretical pattern of a nervous system that might act in the way required. If the robot responded incorrectly to optical, acoustic or tactile stimuli from the environment, it would show that this theoretical pattern was wrong. Protracted calculations and experiments, however, finally resulted in the construction of a robot which went 'looking for food' of its own accord.

The only direct human intervention in its behaviour consists of switching it on. One of the small lamps visible from the exterior which indicate its 'state of mind' shows that it is fast asleep and nothing happens at all. A weak light or a low whistle leaves it unaffected. But a bright ray of light striking its artificial eye causes it reluctantly to turn away.

After about three minutes it slowly begins searching for

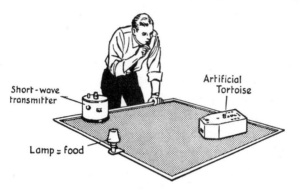

Short-wave transmitter

Artificial Tortoise

Lamp = food

Artificial tortoise on exercise table.

food; it is waking up, so to speak. If it detects a bright source of light, it steers resolutely towards it, for its maker built into its wire nervous system the knowledge that a bright light stands for a source of food. He also provided it with the 'hereditary' or constitutional knowledge that such a 'source of food' must be sought by the shortest route.

If it meets obstacles on the way, such as a piece of wood or a wire fence, it uses its sense of touch to find a way round them. It is now ready to be 'taught' something. Every time it catches sight of a bright light, it is made to hear a whistle. At first it makes nothing of it. But after the sixth time it has grasped the fact that the whistle has something to do with food. Just like Pavlov's dog, the sound of a whistle is sufficient to make it search for food, until it discovers the bright light and makes a bee-line for it.

235

Hans Kretz next tried playing a trick on his robot. He whistled, but offered it no food (represented only by a feeble light). The robot searched in all directions, swivelling this way and that. Hans Kretz went on with his deception, but after the seventh time the robot got disheartened and failed to respond. Kretz could now go on whistling as much as he liked, but it made no difference; the robot refused to budge.

But, if it were left alone for a few minutes, it forgot the trick played on it, and a whistle again made it bustle about, eagerly looking for a bright light.

Mathematics of the Emotions

It will not be surprising if scientists are soon able to construct models with much more complicated modes of behaviour, such, for instance, as moth-like flying robots, which take evasive action on 'hearing' slight ultrasonic sounds or nose-dive when the ultra-high noises grow louder, and it is perfectly conceivable that they might construct an artificial migrant bird, an electronic blackcap with a built-in internal clock, able to recognise the position of certain stars and navigate by them on a course previously decided by man.

Still more interesting is the idea of creating an artificial community life among robot animals. Tin grasshoppers might be made to chirp in such a way as to understand each other's language, 'male' and 'female' might entice one another and male rivals chase each other away. It seems not impossible to stock a whole farmyard with robot fowl. Each could be provided with rather different 'character traits', and one could then see what the effect would be on the pecking order.

The production of artificial moths, grasshoppers, birds and other animals would of course present many problems, and is fundamentally unnecessary. Hans Kretz himself says that the construction of his artificial tortoises is no more than a higher kind of game. He says that for scientific purposes it is sufficient to study animal behaviour theoretically, calculating with electronic brains.

236

Huge electronic computers have now been used for years in the United States to stage theoretical exercises in nuclear warfare between the great powers. The total military and economic potential of contending nations can be presented in columns of figures. The possible moves and counter-moves of a potential enemy can be objectively calculated, together with the direct and indirect consequences.

American electronic experts are able to calculate the effect on the national economy of a rise in the bank rate, the possible consequences of a particular tariff policy, a strike or an acceleration of nuclear armament. Every variable in the complex structure of the economy can be taken into account. The consequences of every possible measure can be calculated in advance by the machine.

Inferences can similarly be drawn about the behaviour of a large number of animals in a poultry-yard, for instance, and calculations can be made showing all the phases through which such a complicated phenomenon as a pecking order is established. Combats between individual chickens, the gesture of humility and the crow of triumph, need only happen on tape and punched cards and in electronic control mechanisms, and the outcome will be known theoretically before the live animals out in the yard have adopted their first posture.

Pressing a few buttons is capable of revolutionising the whole social order of a farmyard. What happens if all the hens suddenly become broody? What are the deeper reasons for the degeneration of the community life of rats in conditions of over-population? To what extent can experience influence the primitive force of instinct? How do the instincts asleep in the subconscious affect modes of behaviour apparently controlled solely by reason?

Such are the problems that await an answer in the foreseeable future. A new type of zoologist is taking his place on the stage, the behaviour cybernetician, who aims at analysing and calculating the emotions and actions of animals exactly as the astronomer analyses and calculates the course of the

237

constellations, the age of the stars and the size of the universe.

We are only at the initial stage of this development. The real goal lies in the distant future – the human mind with all its aberrations. Some day we shall be able to ask not only 'why man and woman get on so badly', but also why mind and body get on so well.

LIST OF SOURCES AND SUGGESTIONS
FOR FURTHER READING

The scientific papers which have been used for this book were published for the most part in periodicals. *The Mysterious Senses of Animals* attempts for the first time to bring them together for a wider circle of readers. The latest findings are published, as they occur, in the following periodicals:

American Scientist, Princeton, New Jersey

Behaviour, Leyden, The Netherlands

Mitteilungen aus der Max-Planck-Gesellschaft zur Förderung der Wissenschaften, Göttingen, Germany

Natural History, The American Museum of Natural History, New York

Natur und Museum (until December 31, 1961: *Natur und Volk*), journal of the Senckenbergische Naturforschende Gesellschaft, Frankfurt (Main), Germany

Die Naturwissenschaften, journal of the Max-Planck-Gesellschaft zur Förderung der Wissenschaften, of the Gesellschaft Deutscher Naturforscher und Ärzte, Berlin-Wilmersdorf, Germany

Naturwissenschaftliche Rundschau, Stuttgart, Germany

Scientific American, New York

Das Tier, Stuttgart, Germany

Die Umschau in Wissenschaft und Technik, Frankfurt (Main), Germany

Zeitschrift für Tierpsychologie, Berlin, Germany

Zeitschrift für Vergleichende Physiologie, Berlin-Wilmersdorf, Germany

Further information on subjects discussed in this book may be found in the selected scientific works and works of popular science listed below.

General Reading

Beach, F. A., *Hormones and Behavior*, Cooper Square Publishers, New York, 1961.

Dobzhansky, Theodosius, *Evolution, Genetics and Man*, John Wiley & Sons, Inc., New York; Chapman & Hall, Ltd., London, 1957.

Dobzhansky, Theodosius, *Mankind Evolving*, Yale University Press, New Haven, 1962.

Fränkel, G. S., and Gunn, D. L., *The Orientation of Animals*, Dover Publications Inc., New York, 1961.

Giersberg, Hermann, *Hormone. Verständliche Wissenschaft*, XXXII, Springer, Berlin, 1953.

Hediger, Heini, *Beobachtungen zur Tierpsychologie im Zoo und im Zirkus*, F. Reinhardt Verlag, Basel, 1961.

Knaurs Tierreich in Farben, 7 vols., Droemersche Verlagsanstalt Th. Knaur Nachf., Munich, 1956–61.

Life, Editors of, and Barnett, L., *The Wonders of Life on Earth*, Time, Inc., New York, 1960 (distributed by Prentice-Hall, Inc.).

Lorenz, Konrad, *Das sogenannte Böse. Zur Naturgeschichte der Aggression*, Dr. G. Borotha-Schoeler Verlag, Vienna, 1963.

Macdonald, J. D., Goodwin, D., and Adler, H. E., *Bird Behavior*, Sterling Publishing Co., New York, 1963.

Maier, N. R. F., and Schneirla, T. C., *Principles of Animal Psychology*, McGraw-Hill Publishing Co., New York, 1935.

Milne, L. J. and M., *The Senses of Animals and Men*, Atheneum, New York, 1962.

Pinner, Erna, *Born Alive*, Jonathan Cape, London, 1959.

Remane, Adolf, *Das soziale Leben der Tiere*, Rowohlts Deutsche Enzyklopädie, Hamburg, 1960.

Roe, Anne, and Gaylord Simpson, George, Editors, *Behavior and Evolution*, Yale University Press, New Haven.

Rostand, Jean, and Bodin, Paul, *Life, the Great Adventure*, Charles Scribner's Sons, New York, 1956.

Scott, J. P., *Animal Behavior*, University of Chicago Press, Chicago, 1958; Cambridge University Press, Cambridge, 1958. (Also reprinted in paper covers, Natural History Press, 1963.)

Tembrock, Günther, *Grundlagen der Tierpsychologie*, Akademie-Verlag, Berlin, 1962 (Eastern Berlin).

Thorpe, W. H., *Learning and Instinct in Animals*, Methuen and Co., London, 1963.

Tinbergen, N., *Social Behavior in Animals*, Methuen & Co., London, 1953.

Tinbergen, N., *The Study of Instinct*, Clarendon Press, Oxford, 1951.

Warden, C. J., Jenkins, T. W., and Warner, L. H., *Comparative Psychology*, 2 vols., Ronald Press, New York, 1936.

Chapter 1

Alpers, Antony, *A Book of Dolphins*, John Murray, 1960.

Blume, D., 'Über die Lebensweise einiger Spechtarten', *Journal f. Ornithologie*, 102, Sonderheft, 1961.

Burnett, A. L., 'Enigma of an Echinoderm', *Natural History*, LXX (1961), pp. 10–19.

Evans, Howard E., 'Predatory Wasps', *Scientific American*, CCVIII (April 1963), pp. 144–54.

Griffin, D. R., *Listening in the Dark*, Yale University Press, New Haven, 1958.

Griffin, D. R., 'More About Bat "Radar"', *Scientific American*, CXCIX (July 1958), pp. 40–4.

Griffin, Donald R., 'Echo-Ortung der Fledermäuse, insbesondere beim Fangen fliegender Insekten', *Naturwiss. Rundschau* (May 1962), pp. 169–73.

Heatwole, Harold, Davis, Donald M., and Wenner, Adrian M., 'The Behaviour of Megarhyssa, a Genus of Parasitic Hymenopterans', *Zeitschr. f. Tierpsychologie*, 19 (1962), pp. 652–64.

Kellogg, W. N., *Porpoises and Sonar*, The University of Chicago Press.

Kolb, A., 'Sinnesleistungen einheimischer Fledermausarten', *Zeitschr. f. vergl. Physiol.*, 44 (1961), p. 550.

Lilly, John C., *Man and Dolphin*, Doubleday & Co., New York, 1961; Gollancz, London, 1962.

Lissmann, H. W., 'Electric Location by Fishes', *Scientific American*, CCVIII (March 1963), pp. 50–9.

Roeder, K. T., and Treat, A. E., 'The Detection and Evasion of Bats by Moths', *American Scientist*, XLIX (1961), pp. 135–48.

Roeder, K. T., *Nerve Cells and Insect Behavior*, Harvard University Press, Cambridge, Mass., 1963.

Schneider, H., and Möhres, F. P., 'Die Ohrbewegungen der Hufeisenfledermäuse und der Mechanismus des Bildhörens', *Zeitschr. f. vergl. Physiol.*, 44 (1960), pp. 1–40.

Schwartzkopff, J., 'Die Stufenleiter des Hörens', *Umschau* (January 1960), pp. 4–7.

Smith, S. L., 'Clam-digging Behaviour in the Starfish', *Behaviour*, 18 (1961), pp. 148–51.

Vincent, F., 'Études préliminaires de certaines émissions acoustiques de Delphinus delphis L. en captivité', *Bulletin de l'Institut Océanographique, Monaco*, No. 1172.

Wimsatt, W. A., 'Bats', *Scientific American*, CXCVII (November 1957), pp. 105–14.

Chapter 2

Birukow, Georg, 'Verhalten des Mistkäfers im Wind', *Zeitschr. f. Tierpsychologie*, 15 (1958), p. 275.

Frith, H. J., 'Incubator Birds', *Scientific American*, CCI (August 1959), pp. 52–8.

Frith, H. J., *The Mallee Fowl*, Angus & Robertson, Sydney, N.S.W., 1962.

Grundfest, H., 'Electric Fishes', *Scientific American*, CCIII (October 1960), pp. 115–24.

Halsband, E., 'Elektrischer Strom zum Scheuchen und Leiten von Fischen', *Umschau*, 16 (1962), p. 513.

Möhres, F. P., 'Die elektrischen Fische', *Natur und Volk*, 91 (1961), pp. 1–13.

Singer, M., 'The Regeneration of Body Parts', *Scientific American*, CXCIX (October 1958), pp. 79–88.

Chapter 3

Edwards, John S., 'Insect Assassins', *Scientific American*, CCII (June 1960), pp. 72–8.

Eisner, T., Monro, A., and Ghent, R., 'Giftige Abwehrstoffe bei Arthropoden', *Journ. Ins. Physiol.*, 6 (1961), p. 272.

Eisner, T., 'Survival by Acid Defense', *Natural History*, LXXI (June–July 1962), pp. 10–19.

Evans, H. E., 'Predatory Wasps', *Scientific American*, CCVIII (April 1963), pp. 144–54.

Evans, H. E., *Wasp Farm*, Natural History Press, New York, 1963.

Graefe, Gernot, 'Das Paarungsverhalten der Weinbergschnecke', *Natur und Museum*, 92 (1962), pp. 139–42.

Hediger, Heini, 'Zum "Schießen" des Schützenfisches', *Natur und Volk*, 91 (1961), pp. 237–43.

Lüling, K. H., 'The Archer Fish', *Scientific American*, CCIX (July 1963), pp. 100–8.

McElroy, William D., and Seliger, Howard H., 'Biological Luminescence', *Scientific American*, CCVII (December 1962), pp. 76–89.

Schaller, Friedrich, 'Weshalb leuchten Glühwürmchen?', *Umschau*, 1 (1961), pp. 4–6.

Schaller, Friedrich, 'Das Licht der Tiere', *Umschau*, 21, 1963, pp. 663–5.

Schildknecht, H., 'Die "Explosionschemie" der Bombardierkäfer', *Angewandte Chemie*, 73 (1961), p. 1.

Wiehle, Hermann, 'Aus dem Spinnenleben Wärmerer Lände', *Die Neue Brehm-Bücherei*, CXXXVIII (1954).

Chapter 4

Eibl-Eibesfeldt, Irenäus, 'Turniere im Tiereich', *Umschau*, 1 (1957), pp. 8–11.

Eibl-Eibesfeldt, I., 'The Fighting Behavior of Animals', *Scientific American*, CCV (December 1961), pp. 112–22.

Gothe, Johannes, 'Zur Droh- und Beswichtigungsgebärde des Kolkraben', *Zeitschr. f. Tierpsychologie*, 19 (1962), pp. 687–91.

Schmidt, Herta, 'Kindliche Komment-Kämpfe als angeborene Verhaltens-
weise?', *Natur und Volk*, 89, 4 (1959), pp. 135–6.

Stokes, A. W., 'Antagonistic Behaviour among Blue Tits at a Winter Feeding
Station', *Behaviour*, 19 (1962), pp. 118–38.

Tembrock, Günter, 'Versuch einer Analyse des Imponierverhaltens beim
Rotfuchs', *Zeitschr. f. Tierpsychologie*, 19 (1962), pp. 577–85.

Thomas, 'Kommentkämpfe zwischen Kreuzotter-Männchen', *Die Naturwissenschaften*, 42 (1955), p. 539.

Chapter 5

Bölsche, Wilhelm, *Der Termitenstaat*, Kosmos-Verlag, Stuttgart, 1951.

Fischer, Heinrich, *Lebensbilder aus der Insektenwelt*, Kosmos-Verlag, Stuttgart,
1954.

Goetsch, Wilhelm, 'Die Staaten der Ameisen', *Verständliche Wissenschaft*,
Springer Verlag, Berlin, 1953.

Güßwald, K., and Kloft, W., 'Radioaktive Isotope zur Erforschung des
Staatenlebens der Insekten', *Umschau*, 58 (1958), pp. 743–5.

Lüscher, M., 'Air-Conditioned Termite Nests', *Scientific American*, CCV
(July 1961), pp. 138–45.

Schmidt, Hans, *Termiten*, Brehm-Bücherei, Leipzig, 1953.

Schneirla, T. C., 'The Behavior and Biology of Certain Nearctic Doryline
Ants', *Zeitschrift f. Tierpsychologie*, 18 (1961), pp. 1–32.

Wallis, D. I., 'Food-sharing Behaviour of the Ants', *Behaviour*, 17 (1961),
pp. 17–47.

Chapter 6

King, J. A., 'The Social Behavior of Prairie Dogs', *Scientific American*, CCI
(October 1959), pp. 128–40.

Chapter 7

Bjerre, Jens, *Kalahari*. Translated from the Danish by Estrid Bannister.
Michael Joseph, London, 1960.

Hoesch, Walter, 'Über Ziegen hütende Bärenpaviane', *Zeitschr. f. Tierpsychologie*, 18 (1961), pp. 297–301.

Rheingold, Harriet L., *Maternal Behavior in Mammals*, John Wiley & Sons,
New York, 1963.

Schneider, Karl Max, *Tiere haben das Wort*, Urania-Verlag, Leipzig, 1957.

Washburn, S. L., and DeVore, I., 'Social Behavior in Baboons and Early
Man', in S. L. Washburn (ed.), *Social Life of Early Man*. Wenner-Gren
Foundation for Anthropological Research; Viking Fund Publications in
Anthropology, XXXI, New York (1961).

Washburn, S. L., and DeVore, I., 'The Social Life of Baboons', *Scientific American*, CCIV (June 1961), pp. 62–71.

Further suggested reading on great apes in the wild:

Goodall, Jane, 'My Life Among Wild Chimpanzees', *National Geographical Magazine* CXXIV (August 1963), pp. 272–308.

Kortlandt, Adriaan, 'Chimpanzees in the Wild', *Scientific American*, CCVI (May 1962), pp. 128–38.

Schaller, George B., *The Mountain Gorilla*, The University of Chicago Press, 1963.

Chapter 8

Alexander, R. D., 'Angriffs-, Revier- und Geschlechtsverhalten bei Feldgrillen', *Behaviour*, 17 (1961), pp. 130–223.

Baeumer, Erich, 'Rangordnung bei Hühnern', *Zeitschr. f. Tierpsychologie*, 12 (1955), p. 387.

Baeumer, Erich, 'Das Kampfverhalten des Hahnes', *Zeitschr. f. Tierpsychologie*, 16 (1959), p. 284.

Fehringer, Otto, 'Rangordnung bei Vögeln', *Naturwiss. Rundschau*, 15 (1962), pp. 19–21.

Guhl, A. M., 'The Social Order of Chickens', *Scientific American*, CXCIV (February 1956), pp. 42–60.

Haas, Adolf, 'Das Verhalten des Malabar-Bärblings', *Zeitschr. f. Tierpsychologie*, 13 (1956), p. 31.

Menzel, R., and Menzel R., 'Über Interferenzerscheinungen zwischen sozialer und biologischer Rangordung', *Zeitschr. f. Tierpsychologie*, 19 (1962), pp. 332–55.

Chapter 9

Calhoun, J. B., 'Population Density and Social Pathology', *Scientific American*, CCVI (February 1962), pp. 139–48.

Frank, F., 'Untersuchungen über den Zusammenbruch von Feldmausplagen', *Zool. Jahrbuch. Syst.*, 82 (1953).

Lorenz, Konrad, *Das sogenannte Böse*, Chapter: Die Ratten, Dr. G. Borotha-Schoeler Verlag, Vienna, 1963, pp. 241–54.

Chapter 10

Baeumer, Erich, 'Lautäußerungen des Haushuhns', *Zeitschr. f. Tierpsychologie* (1962), pp. 394–416.

Frings, H., and Frings, Mabel, 'The Language of Crows', *Scientific American*, CCI (November 1959), pp. 119–31.

Gary, N. E., 'Pheromones of the Bees', *Science*, 136 (1962), p. 773.

Huber, F., 'Die "Sprache" der Grillen und Heuschrecken', *Umschau*, 58 (1958), pp. 42–4 and 101–3.

Jacobs, Werner, 'Über das Singen der Feldheuschrecke', *Zeitschr. f. Tierpsychologie*, 20 (1963), pp. 446–60.

Kainz, Friedrich, *Die 'Sprache' der Tiere*. Ferdinand Enke Verlag, Stuttgart, 1961.

Lorenz, K. Z., 'The Evolution of Behavior', *Scientific American*, CXCIX (December 1958), pp. 67–78.

Lorenz, K. Z., *King Solomon's Ring: New Light on Animal Ways* [Translated from the German by Marjorie Kerr Wilson], Thomas Y. Crowell Co., New York, 1961; Methuen & Co., London, 1961.

Lorenz, K. Z., *Man Meets Dog* [Translated from the German by Marjorie Kerr Wilson], Methuen & Co., London, 1955.

Lüscher, Martin, 'Pheromone als Orientierungsstoffe bei Termiten', *Die Naturwissenschaften*, 47 (1960), p. 503.

Nicolai, Jürgen, 'Familientradition in der Gesangsentwicklung des Gimpels', *Journal für Ornithologie*, 100 (1959), pp. 39–46.

Renner, Max, 'Der Lockstoff der Honigbiene', *Zeitschr. f. vergl. Physiol.*, 43 (1960), p. 411.

Thielcke, Gerhard, 'Vogellaute und -gesänge', *Umschau*, 62 (1962), pp. 335–8 and 365–7.

Thorpe, W. H., *Bird Song: The Biology of Vocal Communication and Expression in Birds*, Cambridge University Press, Cambridge, 1961.

Wilson, Edward O., 'Pheromones', *Scientific American*, CCVIII (May 1963), pp. 100–14.

Chapter 11

Esch, Harald, 'Über die Schallerzeugung beim Werbetanz der Honigbiene', *Zeitschr. f. Vergl. Physiol.*, 45 (1961), pp. 1–11.

Esch, Harald, 'Auch Lautäußerungen gehören zur "Sprache" der Bienen', *Umschau*, 62 (1962), pp. 293–6.

Frisch, Karl von, *Bees: Their Vision, Chemical Senses and Language*, Cornell University Press, Ithaca, New York, 1950; Oxford University Press, Oxford, 1951.

Frisch, Karl von, *The Dancing Bees* [Translated from the German by Dora Ilse], Harcourt, Brace & World, New York, 1961.

Frisch, Karl von, and Lindauer, Martin, 'Über die "Mißweisung" bei den richtungsweisenden Tänzen der Bienen', *Die Naturwissenschaften*, 1961, pp. 585–94.

Frisch, Karl von, 'Dialects in the Language of the Bees', *Scientific American*, CCVII (August 1962), pp. 78–87.

Lindauer, M., *Communication Among Social Bees*, Harvard University Press, Cambridge, Mass., 1961; Oxford University Press, Oxford, 1961.

Lindauer, Martin, 'Kompaßorienrierung', *Ergebnisse der Biologie*, 26 (1963), pp. 158–81.

Wenner, Adrian M., 'Buzzing the Queen', *Scientific American*, CCVII (December 1962), pp. 70–1.

Chapter 12

Altevogt, R., 'Winkerkrabben in Europa', *Umschau*, 59 (1959), pp. 137–9.

Aschoff, Jürgen, and Wever, R., 'Spontanperiodik des Menschen bei Ausschluß aller Zeitgeber', *Die Naturwissenschaften*, 49 (1962), p. 337.

Aschoff, Jürgen, 'Der biologische Tag', *Umschau*, 60 (1960), pp. 129–32.

Brown, F. A., 'The Rhythmic Nature of Animals and Plants', *American Scientist*, XLVII (1959), pp. 147–68.

Bünning, Erwin, *Die Physiologische Uhr*, Springer-Verlag, Berlin, 1958.

Eibl-Eibesfeldt, I., *Galapagos: The Noah's Ark of the Pacific* [Translated from the German by Alan Houghton Brodrick], Doubleday & Co., New York, 1961; MacGibbon & Kee, London, 1960.

Frisch, Karl von, 'Bienenuhr und Blumenuhr', *Zeitschr. f. Tierpsychologie*, 20 (1963), pp. 441–5.

Hastings and Sweeney, 'Endogene Tagesrhythmik bei einem Einzeller', *International Symposium on photoperiodism in plants and animals*, Gatlinburg, Tennessee, 1957.

Hauenschild, C., 'Gibt es bei Tieren mondabhängige Entwicklung?', *Umschau*, 58 (1958), pp. 532–4.

Pizzarello, Donald J., Witcofski, Richard L., and Lyons, E. Ann, 'X Rays and the Time of Day', *Scientific American*, CCVIII (March 1963), p. 78.

Rathmayer, W., 'Endocrine Steuerung des Tagesrhythmus bei Schaben', *Naturwiss. Rundschau*, 15 (1962), pp. 399–400.

Rathmayer, W., 'Ist die Uhr der Tiere ein Oszillator?', *Naturwiss. Rundschau*, 15 (1962), p. 68.

Chapter 13

Bovet, Jacques, 'Influence d'un effet directionnel sur le retour au gîte des Mulots fauve et sylvestre', *Zeitschr. f. Tierpsychologie*, 19 (1962), pp. 472–88.

Buddenbrock, Wolfgang von, *Wie Orientieren sich die Tiere?*, Kosmos-Verlag Stuttgart, 1956.

Carthy, J. D., *Animal Navigation*, Charles Scribner's Sons, New York, 1957; G. Allen & Unwin, London, 1956.

Dörbeck, Friedrich, 'Die Lachswanderung im nördlichen Fernosten', *Natur und Volk*, 85 (1955), pp. 391–9.

Fromme, Hans Georg, 'Untersuchungen über das Orientierungsvermögen nächtlich ziehender Kleinvögel', *Zeitschr. f. Tierpsychologie*, 18 (1961), pp. 205–20.

Geisler, Marianne, 'Untersuchungen zur Tagesperiodik des Mistkäfers', *Zeitschr. f. Tierpsychologie*, 18 (1961), pp. 389–420.

Gerdes, K., 'Richtungstendenzen vom Brutplatz verpflanzter Lachmöwen', *Zeitschr. f. wiss. Zoologie*, 166 (1962), pp. 352–410.

Hasler, Arthur Davis, 'Wegweiser der Zugfische', *Naturwiss. Rundschau*, 15 (1962), pp. 302–10.

Heidenreich, Erich, 'Insekten-Fluktuationen', *Naturwiss. Rundschau*, 14 (1961), pp. 11–14.

Heirtzler, James R., 'The Longest Electromagnetic Waves', *Scientific American*, CCVI (March 1962), pp. 128–37.

Hoffmann, K., 'Richtungsorientierung von Staren unter der Mitternachtssonne', *Zeitschr. f. vergl. Physiol.*, 41 (1959), p. 471.

Johnson, C. G., 'The Aerial Migration of Insects', *Scientific American*, CCIX (December 1963), pp. 132–8.

Matthews, G. V. T., *Bird Navigation*, Cambridge University Press, Cambridge, 1955.

Müller, K., 'Neue Methoden der Fischmarkierung', *Umschau*, 63 (1963), p. 438.

Precht, H., 'Worauf beruht das Heimfindevermögen bei Tieren?', *Umschau*, 61 (1961), pp. 553–5.

Sauer, E. G. F., 'Celestial Navigation by Birds', *Scientific American*, CXCIX (August 1958), pp. 42–7.

Sauer, Franz, 'Die Sternorientierung nächtlich ziehender Grasmücken', *Zeitschr. f. Tierpsychologie*, 14 (1957), p. 29.

Sauer, Franz, 'Zugvögel als Navigatoren', *Naturwiss. Rundschau*, 13 (1960), pp. 88–95.

Schmidt-Koenig, Klaus, 'Die Sonne als Kompaß im Heim-Orientierungssystem der Brieftauben', *Zeitschr. f. Tierpsychologie*, 18 (1961), pp. 221–44; and *Science*, 131 (1960), p. 826.

Schweppenburg, H. Freiherr Geyr von, 'Zur Terminologie und Theorie der Leitlinie', *Journal f. Ornithologie*, 104 (1963), pp. 191–204.

Slijper, E. J., 'Riesen des Meeres', *Verständliche Wissenschaft*, Springer-Verlag, 1962.

Teichmann, H., 'Das Geruchsvermögen des Aales', *Die Naturwissenschaften*, 44 (1957), p. 242.

Tiews, K., 'Thune überqueren die Ozeane', *Information für die Fischwirtschaft*, 6 (1959), p. 97.

Wallraff, H. G., 'Das Orientierungsvermögen der Brieftauben', *Die Naturwissenschaften*, 21 (1957), p. 568.

Williams, C. B., *Insect Migration*, Macmillan Co., New York, 1958; Collins Publishers, London, 1958.

Chapter 14

Eibl-Eibesfeldt, Irenäus, 'Die Verhaltensentwicklung des Krallenfrosches', *Zeitschr. f. Tierpsychologie*, 19 (1962), pp. 385–93.

Hess, E. H., '"Imprinting" in Animals', *Scientific American*, CXCVIII (March 1958), pp. 81–90.

Karli, P., 'Wie verhalten sich Ratten gegen Mäuse?', *Zeitschr. f. Tierpsychologie*, 13 (1956), 323.

Klopfer, Peter H., and Gottlieb, Gilbert, 'Learning Ability and Behavioral Polymorphism within Individual Clutches of Wild Ducklings', *Zeitschr. f. Tierpsychologie*, 19 (1962), pp. 183–90.

Lorenz, Konrad, 'The Evolution of Behavior', *Scientific American*, CXCIX (December 1958), pp. 67–78.

Rowell, T. G., 'The Family Group in Golden Hamsters', *Behaviour*, 17 (1961), pp. 81–94.

Schleidt, Wolfgang, 'Reaktionen von Truthühnern auf fliegende Raubvögel', *Zeitschr. f. Tierpsychologie*, 18 (1961), pp. 534–60.

Schleidt, Wolfgang, 'Die historische Entwicklung der Begriffe "Angeborenes auslösendes Schema" und "Angeborener Auslösemechanismus"', *Zeitschr. f. Tierpsychologie*, 19 (1962), pp. 697–722.

Schneider, Karl Max, 'Jungenfürsorge bei Eisbären', *Zeitschr. f. Tierpsychologie*, 14 (1957), p. 533.

Schremmer, Friedrich, 'Bemerkenswerte Wechselbeziehungen zwischen Orchideenblüten und Insekten', *Natur und Volk*, 91 (1961), pp. 52–61.

Schüz, E., 'Defekte im Brutpflegeinstinkt bei Vögeln', *Zeitschr. f. Tierpsychologie*, 14 (1957), p. 527.

Spindler, Paul, 'Die "Kindchen-Reaktion", ein Teil des menschlichen Brutpflegeverhaltens', *Umschau*, 62 (1962), pp. 636–7.

Tinbergen, N., 'The Evolution of Behavior in Gulls', *Scientific American*, CCIII (December 1960), pp. 118–30.

Chapter 15

Bein, Hugo, 'Physiologische Grundlagen psychischer Vorgänge', *Naturwiss. Rundschau*, 13 (1960), pp. 383–8.

Bünning, Erwin, 'Die Kybernetik im Reich der Organismen', *Naturwiss. Rundschau*, 13 (1960), pp. 229–30.

Hebb, Donald O., and Milner, Peter, 'Aktivitätsformen des Gehirns und Verhaltensorganisation', *Naturwissen. Rundschau*, 16 (1963), pp. 258–62.

Hess, W. R., *Psychologie in biologischer Sicht*, Verlag Georg Thieme, Stuttgart, 1962.

Holst, Erich von, *Künstlich ausgelöste Stimmungen bei Tieren*, Mitteilungen aus der Max-Planck-Gesellschaft, 1959, pp. 120–32.

Holst, Erich von, 'Die experimentelle Erforschung tierischer Triebe', *Umschau*, 60 (1960), pp. 545–9 and 574–6.

Holst, E. von, and Saint Paul, Ursula von, 'Electrically Controlled Behavior', *Scientific American*, CCVI (March 1962), pp. 50–9.

Kretz, Hans, 'Modelldarstellung biologischer Verhaltensweisen', *Umschau*, 62 (1962), pp. 193–5 and 240–2.

Kretz, Hans, 'Zwei Modelldarstellungen kybernetischer Probleme', *Umschau*, 63 (1963), pp. 42–5.

Olds, J., 'Pleasure Centers in the Brain', *Scientific American*, CXCV (October 1956), pp. 105–16.

Ploog, Detlev, *Die Bedeutung der experimentellen Verhaltensforschung als Grundlagenwissenschaft für die klinische Psychiatrie*, Jahrbuch der Max-Planck-Gesellschaft, Munich, 1963, pp. 130–48.

Schneider, Dietrich, *Vergleichende Rezeptorphysiologie am Beispiel der Riechorgane von Insekten*, Jahrbuch der Max-Planck-Gesellschaft, Munich, 1963, pp. 150–77.

Wettstein, H., 'Neuere Untersuchungen über Lernvorgänge und künstliche Intelligenz', *Umschau*, 63 (1963), pp. 27–8.

Wiener, Norbert, *Cybernetics*, 2nd edition, Massachusetts Institute of Technology, Cambridge, Mass., 1961.

GENERAL INDEX

INDEX OF SCIENTISTS AND OBSERVERS

254